*To B...*
*With ...*
*+ great appreciation*
*Courtenay*

# THE END OF THIS ERA

## A Linkage of Science and Religion

### Prof. Courtenay Bartholomew, M.D.

Queenship

**PUBLISHING COMPANY**
P.O. Box 220 • Goleta, CA 93116
(800) 647-9882 • (805) 692-0043 • Fax: (805) 967-5133
www.queenship.org

IMPRIMATUR

Bishop Sydney A. Charles
St. George's
Grenada
27 November 2008

Library of Congress Number # 2009922211

Published by:
Queenship Publishing
P.O. Box 220
Goleta, CA 93116
(800) 647-9882 • (805) 692-0043 • Fax: (805) 967-5133
www.queenship.org

Printed in the United States of America

ISBN: 978-1-57918-372-7

This book is dedicated to
someone very special,
who on June 8, 2002
invited me to write this book.

## About the Author

**Courtenay Bartholomew** is the emeritus professor of medicine of the University of the West Indies. He is a graduate of University College Dublin, Ireland and is a Fellow of the three Royal Colleges of Physicians (London, Edinburgh and Ireland) and also a Fellow of University College Dublin. He is currently the Director of the Medical Research Centre of Trinidad and Tobago. He has received several scientific awards and honours and has published over 80 papers in scientific journals, including the first cases of AIDS in the Commonwealth Caribbean. He has been a member of UNESCO's International Bioethics Committee and is the author of eight books on Mariology. He has appeared in several Marian videos and as guest speaker in many Marian conferences worldwide.

## Previous Books by the Author

A Scientist Researches Mary, The Ark of the Covenant

A Scientist Researches Mary, Mother and Co-Redemptrix

A Scientist Researches Mary, Mother of All Nations

Her Majesty Mary, Queen of Peace

The Immaculate Heart and Mother Seton's Emmitsburg

The Passion of the Christ and His Mother

The Last Help Before the End of Time

# TABLE OF CONTENTS

As I told you, if men do not repent and better themselves the Father will inflict a terrible punishment on all humanity. It will be a punishment greater than the Flood, such as one will never have seen before. Fire will fall from the sky and will wipe out a great part of humanity, the good as well as the bad, sparing neither priests nor faithful. The survivors will find themselves so desolate that they will envy the dead.

Our Lady of Akita
October 13, 1973
(a Church-approved apparition)

# FOREWORD

It was at the foot of the Cross that the Redeemer bequeathed His mother to be our spiritual mother. It was when He said to John: *"Behold thy mother"* (John 19:27). For more than two decades this *Mother of all Nations* and *Queen of Peace* has been appearing all over the world, crying at times, and pleading with her children to change their ways and return to God. She has warned that this is a time of God's Mercy and that she can no longer hold back the hand of His Justice if we do not respond to her call.

Meanwhile man continues to display an ever increasing disrespect and lack of appreciation of and gratitude for the gift of *life*, which is so taken for granted. Indeed, we live in an era in which the disrespect and devaluation of *life* have spawned the advent of the suicide bomber and *international terrorism* with an increasing incidence of murders worldwide. Truly, we are in the midst of a culture of death.

But the gift of *life* is not ours to destroy. It is by far the most precious gift of the Creator and everyone is responsible for his own life before Him. We are stewards, not owners of that life. So said, I thought it important to highlight the origin of life since there are so many of us who, among other things, do not know from where we came physically and that, for example, we are "star born." It is the death of the stars and their explosions into the stratosphere which is the source of life on Earth. In short, we are recycled stardust, the chemistry of life.

We live in the nuclear age and as a consequence, man now has the power to self destruct with the possibility of the annihilation of several nations from a nuclear exchange. As Pope John Paul II once said: "We are the men and women of an extraordinary time, exhilarating yet full of contradictions. Humanity now has instruments of unprecedented power. We can turn this world into a garden or reduce it to a pile of rubble. Man can use this power for good within the bounds of the moral law or he can succumb to the short-sighted pride of a science which accepts no limits but tramples on the respect due to every human being. Today, as never before in the past, humanity stands at the crossroads."

Never in known human history has there also been such worldwide permissiveness in the societies of today, oversaturated with pornography, prostitution, promiscuity and child abuse, all aided and abetted by the internet. In addition, we cannot help but be also concerned about the threat of the new emerging viruses and retroviruses, especially the virus of AIDS, which are claiming millions of lives today as a result of the degeneration in societal mores. Then there is also the ever increasing numbers of natural disasters. It is as if nature itself is revolting against the disorder of man and is reacting accordingly.

Meanwhile, largely through corrupt governments, the rich are getting richer and the poor poorer. In addition, during the 20th century an estimated 70 million people have died from famines across the world, caused by a combination of political, economic and biological factors, overpopulation, loss of arable land, and war.

And so, perhaps as never before, we are in the era of the four horsemen—war, famine, plague and death (Rev. 6:1-8). In fact, it is reasonable to assume that the sin of this era is greater than at the time of Noah when as a result of seeing that the world was so corrupt, God regretted that He had made man and destroyed him with a flood (Genesis 6:7). History is repeating itself. As Peter prophesied: "By water that world was then destroyed; it was overwhelmed by the deluge. The present heavens and earth are reserved by God's word for fire; they are kept for the day of judgment, the day when godless men will be destroyed" (2 Peter 3: 6-7).

There are those who believe that we are in these "end times" (not the end of the world but the end of an era). Unfortunately, there have also been many who have been crying wolf over the centuries and so, when the wolf truly appears at the door, millions will probably be unprepared and will be eating and drinking, and taking wives and husbands. Of course, it is human not to believe that a punishment like that of the great Flood *may* occur during our lifetime. But it is prophesied that it will happen during someone's lifetime, and therefore why not ours? That is the reality.

This world seems to have lost its way, having forgotten that He who claimed to be the Son of God, the Creator, once said: *"I am the way, the truth, and the life"* (John 14:6). But He also said to the Spanish. mystic, the Venerable Maria de Agreda (1602-1665), as recorded in her four-volume book *The City of God,*: "He who listens to My mother, listens to Me." Unfortunately, her pleas are largely falling on deaf ears.

# Chapter 1

## THE CREATION
## OF THE UNIVERSE

*Where were you when I laid the foundation of the earth? Tell me, if you have understanding. Who determined its measurement— surely you know!... Who laid the cornerstone when the morning stars sang together and all the heavenly beings shouted for joy? Or shut in the sea with doors when it burst out from the womb? ... Have you comprehended the expanse of the earth? Declare, if you know all this.... Do you know the celestial laws of the heavens? Can you establish these rules on earth?* (Job 38:4-33).

President Ronald Reagan once said: "It would have been wonderful to see the world begin." However, the Creator was the only one present on that occasion and it is only after centuries of the collective wisdom of the world's scientists that we have now arrived at an acceptable theory of how the universe may have begun. Indeed, it is only with such knowledge that the prophecies of the "end times" can be better understood. For example, what is meant by the words in Scripture: *"The sun will be darkened, the moon will not shed her light, stars will fall from the sky and the hosts of heaven will be shaken loose"* (Mark 13:24-25)?

In this work, the culmination of my previous books, I will attempt to give a very abbreviated and relatively simplified history of the beginning of time. Indeed, the study of the birth of the universe has enabled me to be in a much better position to understand some of the biblical prophecies of the "end times" and for the reader to have a deeper appreciation of the last chapters of this book. It is the meeting of science and religion.

Surely, no true believer in God should be *totally* disinterested in the origin of life. Unfortunately, too many are. They take life for granted, as it were, and are uninquisitive about who and what we are, and, above all, why we are here. In fact, how many of us sit back in our gardens at night and look up at the sky in amazement at the canopy and panoply of the stars? I, personally, have found that my study of the cosmos has brought me even closer to the Creator and I appreciate ever so much more His awesomeness.

Camille Flamarion, the great French astronomer, once said in 1880: "If humankind—from farmers in the field and toiling workers in the cities to teachers, people of independent means, those who have reached the pinnacle of fame or fortune, even the most frivolous of society women—if they knew what profound inner pleasure awaits those who gaze at the heavens, then France, nay, the whole world, would be covered with telescopes instead of bayonets, thereby promoting universal happiness and peace." Indeed, cosmology explains our existence and, above all, should cause us to be humble and to be in awe of the intelligent Designer of the universe, a Designer with a special concern for human beings.

As early as the fourth century, the theologian and scholar Augustine of Hippo had recognized the responsibility of scientists, and in Book Five of his *Confessions* he criticized them thus: "It seemed to me that the scientists were able to think clearly enough to form a clear judgment of the universe, even though they could not penetrate through to its sovereign Lord. That is because such men fall into pride. They accurately predict the eclipse of the Sun, then fall into a state of eclipse themselves. They neglect to investigate the source of the intelligence by which they conduct their research. Much of what the natural philosophers and scientists are saying about the universe is true, but they show no interest in a devout search for the Truth who put the universe together. So they fail to find Him, or if they do find Him, they do not honour Him as God or give thanks to Him." This was as true then as it is today.

Genesis 1:1 of the Hebrew Bible says: *"In the beginning God created the heavens and the earth."* Modern cosmologists, after decades of scientific enquiry and increasingly advanced technologies, have now been able to calculate that the universe came into existence about 10-15 billion years ago in an explosion which generated a massive quantity of heat. It was Sir Fred Hoyle (1915-2001), an English cosmologist, who in 1950 was the first to call this theory the "Big Bang." Interestingly, Hoyle originally used the expression as a sarcastic remark as he was strongly opposed to the idea of an explosive beginning. He believed that the universe always was and that there was no beginning and no end (the steady state theory of Hoyle). However, much to his surprise and somewhat ironically, the term stuck fast.

Cosmologists believe that the seed from which the universe sprang was unimaginably small, dense and hot, and all the matter we see around us was squeezed into this submicroscopic volume of space smaller than the smallest part of an atom, which itself is comprised of protons, electrons and neutrons. This cosmic mustard seed suddenly began to expand into a fireball of creation and the universe was set in motion. But if we go back to the Big Bang and imagine that all the matter and energy of the universe was concentrated into this tiny ball that exploded to form the universe, where did it come from and how did it come into existence? Science, however, will never be able to answer that question.

One might visualize the universe before the Big Bang as a vast, unlimited sea of nothingness but this is not an accurate description because that "nothingness" must have contained energy. Neither was it quite a vacuum because, by definition, a vacuum contains nothing at all. In fact, literally speaking, the Big Bang and its egg were neither big nor was there any bang as there was as yet no air to carry the vibrations! We do not know nor shall we ever know or understand how this was achieved. This, too, transcends science.

Physicists believe that after the Big Bang the four fundamental forces of nature were initially a combined superforce—the gravitational force, the electromagnetic force (which encourages atoms to join into molecules), the strong nuclear force (which holds atomic nuclei together), and the weak nuclear force (a weak nuclear interaction just weak enough so that hydrogen in the sun burns at a slow and steady rate). All four of these fundamental forces were necessary for our universe to develop its astronomical structure and life and if any of them had even a slightly different strength, we would not have had a universe in which life could be sustained.

If gravity, for example, were much stronger, it would crush living organisms of human size and stars would be small and short-lived. If the nuclear forces were of a few percent weaker, only hydrogen would be stable: there would be no periodic table, no chemistry and no life. Gravity dominates the universe and clusters mass into galaxies, stars and planets. Indeed, it has been the major factor during almost all of the universe's 10-15 billion-year lifetime.

But we still do not know what is gravity; why does anything have weight; what allows gravity to accomplish its task of holding you in your seat and the Earth in orbit around the Sun or by what unimaginable and fine-tuned scientific principle does it work?

Now, in 1917, Einstein faced a confusing problem as he tried to reconcile his theory of gravity and the general theory of relativity with the limited understanding of the universe at the time. Like most of his contemporaries, he was totally convinced that the universe was static—neither expanding nor contracting. When in 1929, Edwin Hubble announced that his data showed that the galaxies were moving apart at a rate directly proportional to their distance from the Milky Way, this was the first direct proof that the universe was indeed expanding. It became known as Hubble's law. Einstein eventually came to admit that he was wrong and confessed that is was "the greatest blunder in my life." After that he wrote not only of the necessity for a beginning, but of his desire "to know how God created this world." "I am not interested in this or that phenomenon or in the spectrum of this or that element. I want to know His thoughts. The rest are details." But, of course, in the Christian Bible the rhetorical question is asked: "Who has known the mind of God?" (Romans 11:34).

Further evidence was provided in the 1960s. Using a radio antenna in Bell Laboratories in New Jersey, USA, two physicists Arno Penzias and Robert Wilson found quite by accident that the sky was full of microwave radio "noise." They came to realize that this was the redshifted remnant of the Big Bang itself – its "echo." Astronomers detected this radiation by pointing radio antennae into space to search for the cosmic microwave background. Microwaves are just like lightwaves but with a frequency of the order of 10,000 million waves per second. The microwave radiometer detects the cosmic background radiation left over from the early stages of the Big Bang expansion. These waves have been moving freely through space since the universe was less than a thousandth of its present size.

But the universe around us is not what it appears to be and only ten percent of ordinary matter is visible to telescopes. In short, there is more than meets the eye in the cosmos. The stars, for example, make up less than one percent of its mass and all the loose gas and other forms of ordinary matter are less than five percent. All we know is that dark matter exists and, among other things, holds together galaxies and larger structures such as galaxy clusters. It is called dark matter because it cannot be seen by the human eye. It almost certainly consists of a hitherto undiscovered mysterious type of elementary particle. On the other hand, dark energy, despite its confusingly similar name, is a separate substance that entered the scientific picture only in 1998. It is spread uniformly through space, exerts a negative pressure and is believed to cause the expansion of the universe to accelerate.

Now, I have restricted this account to the macroscopic world with little details about the microscopic world of the atom (protons, neutrons and electrons). Quantum mechanics is a more recent fundamental theory about the microscopic world. It is the science that explains the behaviour of subatomic particles and teaches that the microscopic world is radically different from the macroscopic visible world. As Fred Adams put it, quantum mechanics is the conceptual framework that describes the nature of things on small-size scales. One remarkable difference is that microscopic things have vague properties. Quantum mechanics says that everything is a matter of probability and that it is never going to be possible, even in theory, to know the actual behaviour of individual particles.

It was this element of unpredictability that made quantum mechanics unacceptable to Einstein. He insisted on viewing the universe as an orderly, predictable place, and general relativity was a perfect reflection of that view. In fact, Einstein's feelings went deep. To him, the quantum system was philosophically and mathematically unequipped to exist in the same universe with general relativity, and in a letter of December 12, 1926 to Max Born, the German theoretical physicist, he wrote: "Quantum mechanics is certainly imposing, but an inner voice tells me that it is not yet the real thing. The theory says a lot, but does not really bring us any closer to the secret of the Old One. I, at any rate, am convinced that He does not throw dice."

It is obvious that what brought about the universe must transcend the universe, that is, exist independently of it. Logically, we must therefore come to the conclusion that an entity *outside* the universe is the only kind that could have created it. As Fred Heeran wrote: "Nothing that is confined to time could have created the cosmos. The Creator must have existed 'before' the beginning of time." Indeed, it is today's scientific belief that prior to the creation of the universe, time and space did not exist and there was total darkness. One may therefore say that time began with the Big Bang and before that there was a *timeless* eternity. In short, once upon a time there was no time!

Of course, such a reality almost seems to be an impossibility as we cannot visualize total spacelessness, timelessness and darkness. As Heinz Pogels once wrote: "The nothingness before the creation of the universe is the most complete void that we can imagine—no space, time or matter existed. Yet this unthinkable void converts itself into a plenum of existence—a consequence of physical laws. But where are these laws written into the void? What tells the void that it is pregnant with a possible universe?"

Time, it is said, is nature's way of preventing everything from happening all at once but it is believed that for the Creator, who is outside of time, there is no future in the sense of what will eventually happen. The future and the past are in the present. The past, present and future are all contained in the eternal. And so, when Jesus said: "Before Abraham was I Am" (John 8:58), he broke all rules of geometrical tenses and expressed, not only his divine name, but his timelessness, his "eternal now."

Interestingly, as far back as the 4th century AD, St. Augustine had proclaimed that the world was made *with* time and not *in* time. That is precisely the modern scientific position. But as Gerald Schroeder, the Israeli physicist, had to confess: "I don't pretend to understand how tomorrow and next year can exist simultaneously with today and yesterday. However, although the Creator may know the future, we are responsible for our choices and the actions that result there-of." This, of course, is because free will and the potential for good or tragedy go hand-in-hand. Our choices, through our free will, therefore affect our futures. In other words, the "God of history" has made us responsible for our own history, our own past, present, and future.

Time always moves in a forward direction. Stephen Hawking, widely regarded as the most brilliant theoretical physicist since Einstein, once used this analogy: "Imagine a cup of water falling off a table and breaking into pieces on the floor. If you take a film of this, we can easily tell whether it is being run forward or backward. If you run it backward, you will see the pieces suddenly gather themselves together off the floor and jump back to form a whole cup on the table. You can tell that the film is being run backward because this kind of behaviour is never observed in ordinary life. If it were, crockery manufacturers would go out of business!

"The explanation that is usually given as to why we don't see broken cups gathering themselves together off the floor and jumping back onto the table is that it is forbidden by the second law of thermodynamics. This says that in any closed system disorder always increases with time. In other words, it was a form of Murphy's law. Things always tend to go wrong! An intact cup on the table is a state of high order, but a broken cup on the floor is a disordered state. One can go readily from the cup on the table in the past to the broken cup on the floor in the future, but not the other way round. This increase of disorder with time is one example of what is called 'the arrow of time,' something that distinguishes the past from the future, giving a direction to time." (In fact, this author sometimes wonders if the reversal of time may not be the process which will be used at the resurrection of the dead!).

Now, following the Big Bang and before galaxies existed, the universe was a humongous cosmic cloud of hydrogen. It was the Big Bang which gave birth to hydrogen. It is the simplest and lightest element in the periodic table. Hydrogen atoms were ten times as numerous as all the other atoms and molecules put together. The highest pressures of the hotter interstellar gas then caused compressions thereby forming dense localized clouds of hydrogen. Once clouds condensed like this, gravity now comes into play, pulling masses together, further condensation takes place and a star is born when this large amount of gas, mostly hydrogen, starts to collapse in on itself due to gravity. To sum up the stages— first a whirling disc of gas, then clouds, condensations, and finally stars. This process is ongoing.

Computer simulations show that in time massive nebulae containing hydrogen formed about two hundred billion stars flattened into an unimaginable spiral-like galactic disc 80,000 light years in diameter and 6,000 light years thick. We call that galaxy the Milky Way, named after the white swatch which we see across the black of the night sky. It is our home in the universe. This took place about 100 million years after the Big Bang. In our galaxy alone there are about 135 billion stars, many larger than our Sun and more than a million miles in diameter. Moreover, the distances between stars are millions of miles apart! So much therefore for Jane Taylor's "Twinkle, twinkle, little star, how I wonder what you are! Up above the world so high, like a diamond in the sky."

At the beginning of the century it was thought that the Milky Way was our only galaxy, but in 1929 the eminent American astronomer Edwin Hubble (1889 -1953) showed the unimaginable to the human mind and vision, namely, that there are about a hundred billion others and each has billions of stars. The closest and largest neighbouring galaxy, M31 in the Andromeda, is two million light years distant. All are fleeing away from one another at breakneck speed as if they are remnants of a once enormous explosion. But if galaxies are all moving away from one another and are evolving from earlier forms, it is therefore logical that they were once together in some dense sea of matter and energy.

But pride of place in our galaxy is our Sun, which is 300 times farther away from us than the Moon and is about 300,000 times more massive than Earth. It is about 10 billion years old. It has a diameter close to a million miles and is 93 million miles away from planet Earth, yet we feel its immense heat that far away. From afar it looks like a large and bright smooth-surfaced torchlight. It isn't. In fact, like all other stars, it is a raging fire, an inferno of flames, spewing out deadly radiations and flares millions of miles into space. The energy generated in the Sun's core takes a million years to reach its surface and every second 700 million tons of hydrogen are converted into helium. However, although active for 4.5 billion years, incredibly, it has enough fuel to go on for a further 5 billion years! It is the super power of our solar system.

Sunspots are larger-than-Earth magnetic storms that blemish the solar surface (see Fig.1). They can unleash as much energy as 10 billion hydrogen bombs. Astronomers have no idea why they occur and in roughly 11-year cycles, which is the usual amount of time from one so-called "solar maximum" (the greatest number of sunspots) to the next. At the sunspot maximum there may be 500 or more a year; at sunspot minimum this figure drops to as low as 50 a year. The next maximum cycle is calculated to peak *in the year 2012*. Most sunspot explosions are known as coronal mass ejections and can cause serious disruptions of satellite and radio communications. There are those who also believe that seismic events (earthquakes

**Fig. 1 A Solar flare**

and volcanoes) and hurricanes are triggered by sharp fluctuations in sunspot activity and that planetary configurations and alignments have a powerful influence on the Sun.

A star (like our Sun) generates energy by the nuclear transmutations taking place in its interior—the sort of thing that takes place in nuclear plants. In the core of a star there is a temperature of over 15 million degrees C. It is difficult to appreciate what a temperature of 15 million degrees C means (water boils at a 100 degrees C). It takes that unimaginable degree of heat to convert hydrogen into helium. The hotter an object becomes, the faster its atoms move and when this critical temperature is reached, the hydrogen atoms move so quickly that when they hit one another they fuse together and thus create helium, the second lightest element. Once there is fusion, there is a star. In fact, it was this discovery in 1938 of how nuclear fires light the skies that led to Hans Berthe (1906-2005) winning the Nobel Prize in 1967 "for his contributions to the theory of nuclear reactions, especially his discoveries concerning the energy production in stars."

Following this fusion there is the collision of one helium nucleus with another in a star, producing a fleeting form of an element called beryllium. Another helium nucleus then collides with this short-lived element, leading to the formation of carbon, the fourth most common element in the universe. Now, the more massive the star is, the hotter it needs to be to balance its gravitational attraction, and the hotter it is, the faster it will use up its fuel and then collapse.

When a star's entire supply of hydrogen has fused into the heavier elements and when the fuel runs out, the outer layers of the star implode and then in rebound explode, literally spewing the stellar debris and dust into space, seeding and enriching the galaxy with massive amounts of *life-giving* elements like carbon, iron, oxygen, nitrogen and other heavy elements—the chemistry of life.

The most massive stars collapse in colossal explosions called supernovae. They then form black holes, so called because that is exactly what they are—black voids in space about four million times as massive as our Sun. The immense gravitational field of these holes is so great that not even light or any other anything can escape from the holes. For example, if a spaceship strayed sufficiently close to a black hole (which could be thousands of miles), it would instantly be drawn into it and vanish completely forever because of gravity. Black holes are gravity's victory over mass. Once an avowed concept of his, Stephen Hawking no longer believes his theory of the 1980s that black holes might offer passage into another universe and he has recently confessed that his reworked theory has ruled out his earlier belief that people could some day use black holes to travel to other universes. "I'm sorry to disappoint science fiction fans, but there is no possibility of using black holes to travel to other universes," he eventually acknowledged.

The solar system is our local family of heavenly bodies. Until recently it was thought to have been composed of one star (the Sun), nine planets comprising Mercury, Venus, Earth (the inner planets), Mars, Jupiter, Saturn, Uranus, Neptune and Pluto (the outer planets), and a ring of debris known as the asteroid belt. However, a tenth planet was recently discovered in 2003 in an ongoing survey at Palomar Observatory's Samuel Oschin Telescope by astronomers Mike Brown, who is the Richard and Barbara Rosenberg Professor of Planetary Astronomy at the California Institute of Technology (CalTech), Chad Trujillo (Gemini Observatory) and David Rabinowitz (Yale University). It has been given the name Eris. It has its own Moon, which has been named Dysnomia. Eris is larger than Pluto, but only just. Using the Hubble Space Telescope, its diameter has been found to be 1490 + 60 miles (Earth's diameter is about 8,000 miles).

Now, after the first few billion years when all the galaxies formed, with a spinning cloud of gas and cosmic dust tiny grains of matter collided and grew into larger and larger clumps. Particles became gravel, gravel became small balls and then tiny planets. Planet Earth is one of these. From radioactivity studies the age of planet Earth can be dated to be about 4.5 billion years. In short, it took that long to change the Earth from a steaming rock to what it is today. Its inside consists of a central core rather more than 3,000 miles in diameter surrounded by a thick rocky shell that for the most part is more rigid than steel.

Inside an already hot Earth, temperatures rose further as decaying radioactive elements were released until the ball became a soupy mass simmering at 2,000 degrees C. Heavier matter such as iron sank towards the center and formed a kilometer superdense solid inner core. This core of molten iron is an excellent electrical conductor. As the planet continued to cool, steam began to rise up from the volcanic rocks to form the seas.

The planet is tilted at an angle of 23 degrees and this particular tilt gives us our seasons. Since at different times of the year different parts of the planet lean either into or away from the sunlight, if the Earth had not been so tilted, vapours from the ocean would move north and south piling up continents of ice. If our moon were also only 10,000 miles closer than its distance of about 250,000 miles, our tides would be so enormous that all continents would be submerged.

Eventually after many eons, a planet Earth with the just-right gravity, radioactivity, magnetic fields and oxygen, et cetera was located at the correct distance from the heat and radiation of the sun to sustain the development of life. For example, if the Sun gave off ten percent less than its present radiation, we would freeze; if it gave ten percent more, we would burn. Astronomers describe the optimal location for life as the circumstellar habitable zone (CHZ). It is considered to be the region around a star where liquid water can persist on the surface of a planet.

The Moon is a spherical rock 2,000 miles in diameter and 250,000 miles away but it does not have an iron core like the Earth. It is a satellite, that is to say, it moves around a nearby circular path around the Earth. It is theorized that late in the stage of formation of the Earth, a massive asteroid, perhaps the size of Mars, crashed into the nearly fully-formed Earth. The rocky mantle of the impactor was ejected into orbit and became the Moon. However, this theory is contested. The time required for it to go once around this path is called a lunar month, which is about 28 days. It plays three pivotal roles that affect the evolution and survival of life on Earth. It stabilizes the tilt of Earth's spin axis and it slows its rate of rotation. Another benefit of Earth's large Moon is the movement of tides, which are due to the gravitational effect of both the Moon and the Sun.

Now, the asteroid belt is a region between the orbits of Mars and Jupiter and may contain over a million objects larger than one kilometer across. They are primordial objects left over from the formation of the solar system; left over rocky matter that orbits the Sun and which has never successfully coalesced into a planet. The largest known asteroids have diameters of between 100 and 600 miles. It is but one nemesis of planet Earth. Asteroids and comets are sometimes nudged by the gravitational pull of nearby planets into orbits that cause them to enter Earth's atmosphere.

In ancient and medieval Europe, meteors were described as bright *"fire balls," "shooting stars,"* or *"falling stars"* from the asteroid belt (see Fig. 2). They are bits of dust or rocks from space that get sucked into Earth's gravitational pull when they come close to it. As they enter our atmosphere and plummet towards the ground, they become bright streaks of light, generate intense heat and burn up before they get close enough to Earth. By definition, a meteor does not strike the Earth, meteorites do. Meteorites come from meteors and when they do, they sink deep into the crust and then explode with the force of nuclear bombs. From early times, the Chinese kept meticulous records of meteor showers. The meteor storm of 1833 was of truly superlative strength. One estimate is that there were over one hundred thousand meteors an hour. Many thought it was the end of the world and referred to the event as "the night the stars fell" (see Fig. 10 page 87).

Beyond the orbit of Neptune lies an even larger and more populous region of minor bodies known as the Kuiper belt, named after the astronomer Gerard Kuiper. But while the asteroid belt is composed primarily of rock and metal, the Kuiper belt objects are composed largely of frozen volatile substances (dubbed "ices"), such as methane, ammonia and water. They are comets, referred to by some as "dirty snowballs" (see Fig. 3 ). In the early days of the creation saga, such comets of water slamming into Earth would

**Fig. 2 Meteor showers (Shooting stars falling to Earth)**

**Fig. 3 Halley's Comet**

have turned instantly into steam. In fact, some astronomers believe that much of the water now on our planet's surface arrived via incoming comets. Yet it is not only water that these comets may have brought. They would have played a role in contributing to the chemical evolution of Earth's crust and may have brought important life-supporting organic molecules onto our planet's surface. Most of these comets are in fairly circular orbits with modest eccentricity, but, like meteors, occasionally a cometary nucleus leaves its fellows and plummets into the inner solar system.

# Chapter 2

## THE ORIGIN OF LIFE

*The Earth brought forth life*

As Fred Adams wrote in his book *Origins of Existence - How Life Emerged in The Universe,* a long time ago when Earth was quite young, the night skies were much busier than the seemingly quiescent heavens of today. The solar system was brimming with large asteroids and comets, which provided an unrelenting supply of ammunition for planetary bombardment. Nightly meteor showers were spectacular and rocky intruders more than ten kilometers across—like the one that would much later enforce the untimely demise of the dinosaurs—were commonplace. The planet's fragile surface experienced catastrophic change on a regular basis. And so, in the beginning there was dust but one day life will return to dust and just as our ultimate genesis was entangled with the birth of the stars and the terrifying tumult of asteroids and meteorites so are we still bound to the cosmos.

Against this violent and destructive backdrop, warm pools of water on the surface teemed with organic chemicals, which continually strived to organize themselves into larger structures. The evolution of simple physical systems into more complex ones continued unabated. In a relatively short time these molecular systems increased their complexity to the point of self-replication and became biological systems, culminating in the everyday miracle that we call *life.*

One of the greatest scientific discoveries ever was the discovery of the structure of DNA by Francis Crick and James Watson. But perhaps even more wonderful was the discovery of the genetic code by Craig Venter and Francis Collins. Indeed, the God of the Bible is also the God of the genome. All living organisms have the wondrous capacity of mobility and replication. The genetic information in organisms is inscripted in molecules called ribonucleic acid

(RNA) and deoxyribonucleic acid (DNA). It is the DNA that is capable of transferring inherited characteristics. Investigations of many organisms, from bacteria to humans, reveal that this genetic "code," by which information in DNA and sometimes RNA is translated into proteins, is universal in all known organisms. There is, however, an idea that the first cell-replicating world was an RNA world that preceded our DNA world in which proteins synthesis became central.

In the Book of Genesis, it simply states that life first appeared on the third day and we are merely told: "The earth brought forth (life)." Earth therefore had within it the necessary properties and ingredients for life to flourish. However, because science had no observers stationed nearby during life's origin, it has tried to answer the question through indirect means.

As we have seen, the elements of the Earth are the elements formed by the violent death of stars, which are dispersed throughout the galaxy, paving the way for the emergence of the universe that we see today. Indeed, we are all the inheritance from earlier generation of stars and the ashes of their nuclear explosions are the materials out of which all living things are made. We live in galaxies whose stars explode to seed space with the building blocks of life. In other words, the *death* of the stars is the source of *life* on Earth. And so, both biblically and scientifically speaking, we are recycled dust, stardust, and whenever we look at the sky at night we should appreciate that in a very literal and physical sense we are part of it all and that there is an exploding star at the start of our family tree. The Book did say: *"And the Lord God formed man from the (star) dust of the ground"* (Genesis 2:7).

So said, it has been found that carbon lies at the centre of life and more than any other element it has the ability to form very massive yet stable molecules. All life on Earth is carbon-based and it is the key ingredient of our biomolecules. Carbon atoms link together in chains and bind with other atoms to make the whole array of organic chemicals that constitute life, from our DNA to our fingernails. It is also the essential stepping stone for the production of the eighty-six natural elements heavier than carbon. Only one other atom is as versatile as carbon and that is silicon. Silicon chip technology exploits these properties and it is therefore no coincidence that silicon intelligence is portrayed as the only possible rival to our own carbon-based brain.

Life is also water-based and it is the substance of most of ourselves (over 50 percent to nearly 90 percent of body weight in direct proportion to body surface area). It takes an active role in most of life's activities. So long as liquid water is available, life is possible. Indeed, 70 percent of Earth's surface is comprised of water. As for oxygen, one theory is that plants did not invent photosynthesis but stole the idea, as it were, from bacteria. Chloroplasts, the organelles performing photosynthesis inside leaves, are descendants of bacteria called cyanobacteria, which are far more ancient than plants and it is believed that they performed photosynthesis at least a billion years before the arrival of plants. It is believed that they released oxygen puff by puff over the billions of years and that the oxygen came from the hydrogen source—water. We are now breathing a life-supported mixture of 20 percent oxygen and 80 percent nitrogen. Ozone, on the other hand, is symbolized as $O_3$, meaning three oxygen atoms chemically bound together. This ozone layer is at an altitude of about 25 kilometers (15 miles) above Earth and ozone is our important shield against the ultraviolet light from the Sun.

Christian de Duve is the Andrew W. Millon professor of the Rockefeller University. He was awarded the Nobel Prize in Medicine in 1974, jointly with Albert Claude and George Palade "for discoveries concerning the structural and functional organization of the cell." His two-volume book *A Guided Tour of the Living Cell* is one of the most beautifully-written treatises on the microscopic world of the trillions of cells that make up the human body. In it he detailed the *microscopic* wonder of the human body, but as he said: "What we have today is a description of what happens in the cell, not an understanding of how it happens. The macroscopic body is what we see exteriorly, however it is at the microscopic and electron microscopic levels that the mind is boggled. Human beings are ambulatory collections of some 100 trillion cells. It would take 32,000 years to count to this number from 0 (one count per second, night and day). It is a marvel beyond human concept, capability and comprehension." As the Greek writer Sophocles (495-406 BC) once wrote: "Numberless are the world's wonders, but none more wonderful than man himself" or as the Psalmist wrote: *"I praise you because I am fearfully and wonderfully made"* (Ps.139:14).

The book *The Home Planet* records the remark of Aleksei Leonov, the first man to walk in space in 1965: "We have come to consider the planet a holy relic." In like manner, Russian cosmonaut Boris Volynov, one of the cosmonauts of the world's first Space Station in 1969, returned to Earth saying: "Having seen the Sun, the Moon, the stars and our planet... you begin to look at things differently and with greater trepidation." Then in July 1969, countless millions all over the world watched Apollo 11 lift off on schedule on a two-and-a-half days quarter million miles journey on a mission to land on the Moon. On Sunday, July 20, Neil Armstrong and Edwin Aldrin landed on the Sea of Peace (Sea of Tranquility). It was man's first step on the Moon. It was a "giant leap for mankind." The fourth manned lunar landing by Apollo 15 was in July 1971. Astronaut James Irwin returned from the Moon and in an emotional speech he testified that he had felt the presence of God there. He then devoted the last two decades of his life to sharing his lunar experience and conversion: "God had a plan for me," he said to a journalist, "to leave Earth and to share the adventure with others, so that they too can be lifted up."

Perhaps if it were possible for all of us to have experienced what these astronauts beheld in space, then man might become more humble, more grateful for the gift of life, in tune with the universe and the laws and ordinances of the Creator, and not as arrogant and self-destructive as he is.

# Chapter 3

## ARE WE ALONE?

*There may be other beings, intelligent, created by God.*
*This does not conflict with our faith because we*
*cannot put limits on the creative freedom of God.*
Fr. Jose Gabriel Funes

What are the chances, scientifically speaking, of life existing outside our solar system? Some would argue that there is little doubt that the universe is populated with intelligences and most of them probably far in advance of our own since we have only been around a relatively short time. Indeed, it seems absurd to think that God made the universe just for us, and there must be habitable zones around other stars where temperatures are neither too cold nor too hot for the existence of liquid water. In fact, according to one astronomer, the Milky Way probably contains at least 10 billion stars that could habour habitable, terrestrial planets.

As Fred Heeran wrote, "given the abundance of stars in the universe (about 200 billion stars) in a galaxy of perhaps 100 billion galaxies in the *visible* universe, and given the abundance of planetary systems, the right conditions must exist in billions of cases." Paul Davies, the renowned physicist and cosmologist, also wrote in his book *Other Worlds*: "The Milky Way contains about 100 billion stars grouped together in a gigantic spiral assembly typical of the billions of other galaxies scattered throughout the universe. It would be surprising if life were not widespread throughout the cosmos." Sir Fred Hoyle joined such thinkers. He wrote: "With so many possible planetary systems, should we not expect the inhabited planets to be moving around some of the nearby stars? We certainly should."

Carl Sagan, the late astronomer of Cornell University, is one example of those who followed this line of reason. Some years ago, he raised private funding for a radio telescope that would search the skies for a message coming in to us from supposed extraterrestrial beings in the hope of letting them know that we are here. Since that time various other attempts to communicate with possible life outside of planet Earth have been made, but without success. By expanding the search for life to places far beyond our own solar system, we can greatly increase the odds that life might be present. At the same time, the odds are that such life will be physically so distant from us that we will never know about it, much less be able to communicate with it. For example, when we say that a star is five, or fifty, or five thousand light years away, we are saying that any signal we send there will take five, or fifty, of five thousand years to arrive and the response would take just as long to get back to us. That kind of time lag makes it hard to get a good conversation going!

Some people may be surprised to learn that today's Catholic Church not only encourages the scientific study of the universe but it even supports its own astronomical observatory. The Vatican Observatory's telescope sits on the roof of the Pope's summer home in Castel Gandolfo, Italy. It was founded by Pope Leo XIII in 1891, and more recently it has also built a new advanced technology telescope on a mountain top at the University of Arizona in Tucson.

Indeed, the well-acknowledged mistake that the Church made in the 16th century trying to silence Galileo is all the more stark when contrasted with the many numerous times and places where Church-supported astronomers did get it right. For example, Pope Gregory XIII used astronomy to reform the calendar in 1582 (by employing reputable astronomers). Seventeenth-century Jesuits invented the reflecting telescope and the wave theory of light, and in the 18th century they ran a quarter of all the astronomical observatories in Europe while their missionaries ran most of the observatories outside Europe. In the 19th century, the Jesuit Angelo Secchi was the first to classify stars and planets by their colour spectra, turning "astronomy into astrophysics," and it was the 20th century priest, George Le Maître, who also suggested that the universe began in a kind of a cosmic explosion that eventually came to be called the "Big Bang" theory.

In his booklet *Intelligent Life In the Universe? Catholic belief and the search for extraterrestrial intelligent life*, first published in 2005, Br. Guy Consolmagno SJ, astronomer in the Vatican Observatory, Vatican State, wrote that he had a hunch that sooner or later the human race will discover that there are other intelligent creatures out there in the universe. Part of his reason for that hunch is scientific. As he argued, there are already hundreds of nearby stars that we know have planets, and there are so many billions of other stars waiting to be explored in our galaxy and so many billions of other galaxies (each with billions of stars) in the *visible* universe, surely, somewhere in that number there must be other civilized, rational beings.

But as Br. Guy asked, why would the Church be interested in astronomy? Certainly, one reason is that the study of creation is a way of knowing the Creator. St. Paul insists that God is revealed to us in the image He has created (Romans 1:20). In this He was echoing a long Jewish tradition that "the heavens proclaim the glory of God" (Psalm 8). Indeed, the German theologian Joseph Pohle argued that the Glory of God *demanded* that the universe be filled with intelligent beings, and not just us.

Fr. Jose Gabriel Funes, the director of the Vatican Observatory, also told *L'Osservatore Romano*: "Life forms could exist in theory even perhaps without oxygen or hydrogen... As there is a multiplicity of creatures on Earth, so there may be other beings, intelligent, created by God. This does not conflict with our faith because we cannot put limits on the creative freedom of God. Science, especially astronomy, does not contradict religion. The Big Bang theory is the most reasonable explanation for the creation of the universe, but God is the creator of the universe and we are not here by chance." He admitted that he is not the first astronomer nor the first religious believer to see the amazing panoply of the stars in the sky at night and intuit that God's creativity could not possibly just stop with us. Indeed, appreciating God as the Creator of a universe big enough to contain those billions and billions of galaxies and stars makes us realize just how immense God's eternity must be.

Now, while it is true that the Bible is specifically the history of God's interactions with us humans, it by no means rules out the existence of intelligent creatures besides humans. In fact, there is nothing in Holy Scripture that could confirm or contradict the possibility of intelligent life elsewhere in the universe. Meanwhile, we are free to speculate as the existence of intelligent life on planets other than Earth neither rules in nor rules out any theological principle. Of course, the existence of human life other than on Earth will raise important theological questions, however, as Br. Guy wrote, theologians, like the rest of the human race, will just have to wait and see. Indeed, it is also very likely that there are many intelligent beings out there, who have been in existence long before planet Earth was populated and who may also be much more (or totally) in tune with the Creator.

# Chapter 4

## SCIENCE RECONCILES WITH GENESIS

*There can be no conflict between science and*
*religion as they both deal with truth.*

But how does one reconcile science and religion with the Book of Genesis? To date, the Big Bang theory is modern science's most favoured theory of beginnings. It describes a creation event that defies atheism and pantheism, and harmonizes with the Bible. George Smoot, leader of the satellite team that first detected the cosmic "seeds" of the universe, had this to say: "There is no doubt that a parallel exists between the Big Bang as an event and the Christian notion of a creation... In fact, the Big Bang theory describes a creation event that defies atheism and pantheism, and harmonizes with the Bible. This theory takes us back to a time when, after the first moment of creation, the entire universe consisted of a region a trillionth the size of a proton."

Among most biblical theologians there is wide agreement that the story of the creation of the world and of mankind in the first chapters of Genesis is presented to recount the beginning of the religious history of the people of Israel and is not a scientific analysis to establish the age or mode of origin of the earth. The fundamentalists would say that the age of the universe is exactly the age derived from the generations as they are listed in the Book of Genesis. For them, the cosmological estimate of the age of the universe, which is now thought to be billions of years, is a preposterous fiction and not in keeping with the Bible, and as far as they are concerned, the time between the beginning and the appearance of man is said to be six days—and six days it is!

However, time as described in the Bible is not the same as we know it today. Old Testament theology talks in the language of the average man at that time while current cosmology makes its statements in modern-day scientific terms and discoveries. As

Gerald Schroeder said in his book *The Science of God*, we find a hint for this in the 2900-year-old Book of Psalms: *"A thousand years in your sight are as a day that passes, as a watch in the night"* (Psalm 90:4). Deep within Psalm 90, there is the truth of this reality. Famous theologians of old whose writings show that they believed that the creation "days" were not "solar days" include Origen, a third century apologist, St. Augustine and St. Basil, 4th century bishops and St. Thomas Aquinas, a 13th century theologian.

According to the Irish Archbishop James Usher (1581-1656), who based his calculations on biblical chronology, the world was created in 4004 BC. However, others such as Leonardo da Vinci, Cyrano de Bergerac and the German philosopher Godthfried Wilhelm Leibniz, were already thinking in terms of much larger timespans and considering the possibility that the universe had been in existence for hundreds of thousands of years, even millions of years, without being capable of proving the fact. It was not until 1905 that Ernest Rutherford suggested that radioactive material could be used to date rocks and when the full series of decayed products of radioactive disintegration was firmly established, it became clear that the earth had to be not millions but billions of years old.

As Fred Heeren wrote, the theological theory of a recent creation rests in great measure upon a single word used in the first chapter of Genesis, the word "day," a word whose intended meaning was open to dispute. Each category of the creative act in the Bible is described as taking place in a "day," but the fact that the word "day" referred to a great period of time rather than a solar day is quite clear. For those Christians who feel the need for support from tradition, it could be pointed out, for example, that centuries ago St. Augustine (4th century AD) had said that the creation "days" were not sun-divided days, but rather God-divided days.

According to Schroeder, whom I quote extensively, the biblical calendar is divided into two sections: the first six days of Genesis and all the time thereafter. The first two chapters of Genesis describe the universe's step-by-step formation in biblical terms and language. A study of the text shows that for the first one or two days of the six days of Genesis, the earth did not even exist, for although Genesis 1:1 says that "in the beginning God created the heavens and the earth," the very next verse says that "the earth was a formless void" (Genesis 1:2). The first verse of Genesis is therefore a general statement meaning that in the beginning a primeval substance was created and from this substance the heavens and the earth would be made during the subsequent six days. This is explicitly stated in Exodus 31:17: "In six 'days' the Lord made the heavens and the earth." Genesis 1:5 then says: "Evening came and morning came: the first day."

Now, this is the first time that a "day" is quantified. "Evening and morning"! Does it mean sunset and sunrise? It would certainly seem so. The biblical text goes on to say the same for the second and the third day. However, it is only on the fourth day that the sun is mentioned. How then can there be such a concept of "evening" and "morning" for the first three days if the sun, the divider of evening and morning, is only mentioned on the fourth day? And so, it is obvious that "day" in the Bible cannot be "day" as we know it to be. This is a very important interpretational point.

As we have seen, it is believed that the universe began with a bang and the empty cosmos, devoid of light and matter, was packed with a powerful dark energy that hurled the universe onward. Photons, on the other hand, are particles that correspond to electromagnetic radiation. They travel at the speed of light and have an energy that depends on their wavelength; the shorter the wavelength, the larger the energy. According to current understanding and conjecture, when the universe was dark the photons were held in a soup of random collisions with masses of free electrons. After several hundred thousand years passed, only when temperatures and photon energies continued to fall in proportion with the universe's expansion and to a level that permitted electrons to bind in orbits around atomic nuclei, did the ubiquitous photon-electron collisions cease. Photons were then freed from long bondage with matter and when the temperatures fell below 300 degrees, they burst forth bathing the universe in a blaze of light. In fact, so fascinated was Einstein about the phenomenon and physics of light that he was often heard to comment: "For the rest of my life I want to reflect on what light is."

Following the initial Big Bang, after several hundred thousand years passed, temperatures and photon energies (the particles of light and other forms of electromagnetic radiation) continued to fall in proportion with the universe's expansion, and when the temperatures fell below 3,000° degrees K, a critical event occurred. Light separated from matter and emerged from the darkness. The universe was then bathed in a sea of light. With this separation of light from matter, matter could now start to coalesce. Life was on its way.

The Bible puts the science this way:

> *The earth was a formless void and darkness covered the face of the deep, while a wind from God swept over the face of the waters. Then God said, "Let there be light," and there was light. And God saw that the light was good; and God separated the light from the darkness. God called light day, and the darkness he called night. And there was evening and there was morning, the first day*
> (Genesis 1:2-5).

When the matter of the universe was freed from the constant bombardment by photons and there was diffuse matter, mainly the nebulous gases of hydrogen (75%) and helium (25%), fusion among the nuclei started the nuclear furnaces, which we call stars or suns, and which still dot our night skies with light. Meanwhile as the earth continued to cool, steam began to rise up from the earth and the volcanic rocks to form the seas. In keeping with this science, the Bible says:

> *And God said: "Let there be a dome in the midst of the waters and let it separate the waters from the waters." So God made the dome and separated the waters that were under the dome from the waters that were above the dome. And it was so. God called the dome sky. And there was evening and there was morning, the second day*
> (Genesis: 1:6-8).

This was the dome-shaping of the galactic disc of the Milky Way with most of the stars in the dome. Eventually from this stellar fusion came all the elements present in our universe in addition to hydrogen and helium — carbon, nitrogen, oxygen, iron, et cetera. In fact, the human body is composed mainly of oxygen (65%), carbon (18%), hydrogen (10%), nitrogen (3%) and smaller percentages of calcium, potassium, sodium, iron, et cetera.

Fossil evidence has now confirmed that the first simple plant life appeared immediately after liquid water. This is in perfect agreement with the biblical account of this period, which mentions the first liquid period on Earth when the oceans and dry land appeared. Light and water are the prerequisites for the photosynthetic growth of plants and a by-product of photosynthesis is the release of molecular oxygen. It was on the third day of Genesis that plant life appeared. Early bacteria and plants probably produced the oxygen, which enriched and changed the atmosphere. This allowed for further development of life. The Bible states it this way:

> And God said: "Let the waters under the sky be gathered into one place, and let the dry land appear." And it was so. God called the dry land the earth, and the waters that were gathered together he called the seas. And God saw that it was good. Then God said, "Let the earth put forth the vegetation; plants yielding seed, and fruit trees of every kind on Earth bearing fruit with seed in it." And God saw that it was good. And there was evening and there was morning, the third day
> (Genesis 1:9-13).

It was only on the fourth day that the two great luminaries appeared in the firmament of heaven. The Bible relates that the sun, moon and stars were either made during this period or that they were already present but only became visible during this period. Indeed, the text tells us that they became so clearly visible that they could be used for telling time and seasons. This biblical account was obviously from an earthly viewpoint because the earth is the only celestial body close enough to the moon and the sun to see them as great luminaries. The Bible says:

> And God said: "Let there be lights in the dome of the sky to separate the day from the night; and let them be for signs and for seasons and for days and years..." And it was so. God made the two great lights—the greater light to rule the day and the lesser light to rule the night—and the stars. God set them in the dome of the sky to give light upon the earth. And God saw that it was good. And there was evening and there was morning, the fourth day
> (Genesis 1:14-19).

The biblical sequence then records that animal life appeared in the waters for the first time on day five. This is after the sun became visible in the firmament of heaven on day four. This is also in keeping with the scientific conclusions. During this period the atmosphere consisted of photosynthetically-produced oxygen, which rose to concentrations comparable to today's atmosphere. And so, the earth brought forth life. In short, the earth had within it the necessary properties for life to flourish. Indeed, as I have said before, the universe was created for life from its very inception. The waters then swarmed abundantly with many types of animals. It was at this time that reptiles and winged animals appeared. The Bible says:

> And God said: "Let the waters bring forth swarms of living creatures, and let birds fly above the earth across the dome of the sky. So God created the great sea monsters and every living creature that moves... and God saw that it was good. God blessed them, saying, "Be fruitful and multiply and fill the waters in the seas, and let birds multiply on the earth." And there was evening and there was morning, the fifth day. Then God said: "Let the earth bring forth living creatures of every kind: cattle and creeping things and wild animals of the earth of every kind." And it was so...And God saw that it was good (Genesis 1: 20-25).

Finally, humankind appeared on day six.

> And God said: "Let us make man in our image, according to our likeness; and let them have dominion over the fish of the sea, and over the birds of the air, and over the cattle, and over all the wild animals of the earth, and over every creeping thing that creeps in the earth." So God created humankind in his image, in the image of God he created them, male and female he created them... And it was so. God saw everything he had made, and indeed it was **very** good. And there was evening and there was morning, the sixth day (Genesis 1: 26-31).

Hominids had roamed the earth for some 300,000 years in our space-time reference frame, but neither the Neanderthals nor the Cro-Magnons evolved into human beings. At a crucial point in time, when the earth was more "user friendly," the Creator improved the species genetically, morphologically and spiritually. A quantum leap and change occurred and the name chosen for the first of the species *Homo sapiens sapiens* was Adam. A special ingredient not mentioned before is summoned at this junction. God injected an extra "spiritual" ingredient. He "breathed" the soul of life into Adam and man then became a special living being. Indeed, we are spiritual beings, but embodied. No direct linkage to the hominid predecessors has been discovered and the link is still missing.

Now, the "soul" is called the "breath of God" because it is created by God in its spiritual or breath-like nature. It is believed that man's predecessors, although physically related, were not connected by a spiritual line of evolution. It is this that has set mankind apart from the other animals, and so, as Shroeder said, perhaps, to be more accurate, modern man should be re-labeled *Homo sapiens sapiens spiritus* for he is a spirit-indwelled being.

As the Bible says:

*Yahweh God formed man from the dust of the ground.*
*Then he breathed into his nostrils the breath of life; and*
*man became a living being* (Genesis 2:7).

And so, in the biblical narrative we see that creation flowed from chaos to cosmos, a flow from disorder towards increasing order in the universe until it was not only good, but eventually *very* good on the sixth day. The long physical course of creation was prepared for its ultimate purpose—*life*. The environment for humankind was in place. It was created by the Master Physicist, Mathematician, Engineer, Architect, Biologist and Chemist.

As Fred Heeren wrote: "In this century science is finally catching up with what the Bible has taught us all along. The two most fundamental discoveries of 20th century science—that the universe had a beginning and that it has been fine-tuned for life—are also the two primary teachings of Genesis 1. And here we learn, as the key feature of each stage of creation, that 'it was good.' And when all parts were completed and working together in preparation for conscious life, 'it was **very** good.'"

According to the Bible, on the seventh "day" God rested from all the work that He had done in creation (Genesis 2:3). Indeed, it can be said that He has not created any additions to the universe since Adam and Eve. In a sense, therefore, we are still in the seventh day. But He is ever creating souls.

Now, when the physical universe was prepared and mankind

was in place, from that time onward there would be an interplay between man and his knowledge of the will of the Creator. But man had to be given a free will. The "democratic" God had no choice. And so, although the Creator knows the future, we are responsible for our choices and the actions that result therefrom. As Heeren philosophized: "So what might a super-intelligent, caring Creator do? Make creatures who have no wills of their own so that they cannot bring evil into His perfect universe? Not if God desired to have an eternal relationship with the people who would *willingly* return His love. The very idea of a real will to love requires the real possibility of a person's will to reject it."

In *Show Me God*, Heeren rationalizes that "true love requires mutual choice. If God desired to have an eternal, trusting relationship with people who would willingly return His love, He would not simply create a people filled with love and trust that will not involve their wills. The very idea of a real will to trust and love requires the real possibility of a will to distrust and reject. Such acceptance or rejection can only come with real opportunity in life. God gives this opportunity, this call, to everyone; but He chooses for eternity (with Him) only those who willingly accept and trust Him." (And I may add, "love Him"). "What then might be God's options after his race of free-will creatures broke the harmony of his universe? He could exterminate them. He could simply overlook their injustices. He could leave them alone and let them try to straighten out themselves. But none of these options show the forethought of a perfect, super-intelligent, caring Creator. What then did God do? *He died for us.* There is no greater love. He showed both perfect justice and endless mercy. And by so doing, He gave those who wanted to be reconciled to Him the chance to be forever changed, to be eventually made into fit company for Him throughout eternity. This was His predestined plan before time began."

In December 1968, three astronauts set off on a mission to orbit the moon. In a historic broadcast to Earth on Christmas eve, Major William Anders, in wondrous rapture over the view in space, was heard reading from the Book of Genesis the passage describing the creation of the world: *"In the beginning, God created the heavens and the earth..."* Then from a quarter of a million miles out in space, Captain James Lovel continued: *"And God called the light day and the darkness he called night..."* Colonel Frank Borman completed the reading with the verse: *"And God said, let the waters under the heavens be gathered unto one place and let the dry land appear also."* It was a new dawn for them as they looked down in awe on God's creation of a universe—destined for *life* from its inception.

# Chapter 5

## SCIENTISTS AND RELIGION

*A little science takes one away from God,*
*but a great deal of science brings us back to Him.*

There is the notion that most scientists are atheists or evolutionists, however, this has not been my experience. Outside of the communist countries, which indoctrinate their citizens in atheism, most scientists are believers although many of them may not strictly follow their various religious practices and seem, as it were, to be more interested in science than in the God. The God of science.

As I said before, as early as the fourth century AD, St. Augustine of Hippo recognized that trait among scientists and in Book Five of his *Confessions,* he criticized them thus: "It seems to me that the scientists were able to think clearly enough to form a clear judgment of the universe, even though they could not penetrate through to its sovereign Lord. That is because such men fall into pride. They accurately predict the eclipse of the sun, then fall into a state of eclipse themselves. They fail to investigate the source by which they conduct their research. Much of what the natural philosophers and scientists are saying about the universe is true, but they show no interest in a devout search for the Truth who put the universe together. So they fail to find him, or if they do find Him, they do not honour Him as God nor give thanks to Him."

Now, much of the world's unease today has in part been caused by the rapid advancement of science and technology and the tendency by some to divorce science from religion and the supernatural. This unrest will continue and ever increase unless those who profess to speak in the name of science learn to humble themselves in the presence of Eternal Wisdom. As Louis Pasteur once observed: "A little acquaintance with science distances us from God; greater acquaintance with science brings us even closer."

Albert Einstein is also recorded as saying: "Religion without science is blind. Science without religion is lame." He also once remarked that "God does not play dice." In similar view, Sir Fred Hoyle, the British astronomer, came to the conclusion that for the first cell to have originated by chance is as likely as the assembly of a 747 Jumbo Jet by a tornado swirling through a junkyard full of airplane parts. Chance could not have formed life.

Nobel laureate Sir Francis Crick, co-discoverer of the structure of the DNA molecule, also wrote in his book *Life Itself*: "The origin of life appears to be almost a miracle, so many are the conditions which would have had to be satisfied to get it going. We have to wonder at the intricacy of life's cellular workings. The most optimistic scenarios reveal that random reactions on their own could not have produced life in the time available even if the entire universe was a laboratory for these random reactions. Indeed, the list of numerical 'accidents' that appear necessary for life and the existence of the universe is exhausting, and the numerical coincidences must remain the most compelling evidence of cosmic design (in other words, intelligent design)."

Indeed, the scientific laws of the universe are so very precise that they result in perfect symmetry, harmony and balance. Such a finely-controlled creation defies both atheism and all the religions of pantheism. As Francis Bacon once said: "God never wrought miracles to convince atheism because his ordinary works have certainly convinced it." Gerald Schroeder also wrote: "Our universe, tuned ever so accurately for the needs of intelligent life, ticks to the beat of a very skilful Watchmaker." And so, as is often said, since the complexity of a watch requires a watchmaker, how much more so does the complexity of the human body and mind, indeed, of creation?

However, on its own, science and theology cannot solve the mystery of the origin of the universe—and never will. It is the old tale (attributed to Dr. Robert Jastrow, founder of NASA's Goddard Institute and Director of Mt. Wilson Institute) of the scientists who scaled a huge mountain in their inquiry into the origin of the universe. They are about to conquer the highest peak. As they pull themselves over the final rock, they are greeted by a band of theologians, who have been just sitting there for centuries— perplexed!

The fascinating and informative book *Cosmos, Bios, Theos—Scientists Reflect on Science, God, and the Origins of the Universe, Life and Homo sapiens* by Roy Abraham Varghese and Henry Margenau contains varied and exciting replies of 60 leading scientists (including 24 Nobel prize winners) to questions related to religion and science. Professor Sir Neville Mott, the 1997 winner of the Nobel Prize for Physics with Phillip W. Anderson, and John Van Vleck "for their fundamental theoretical investigations of the electronic structure of magnetic and disordered systems," wrote: "The concept of the Big Bang and what followed it are strongly supported by observations. Where religion has opposed the findings of science, it has almost always had to retreat. I thought then, and still do, that science can have a purifying effect on religion, freeing it from beliefs from a pre-scientific age and helping us to a truer concept of God."

Dr. Arno Penzias, the 1962 Nobel Prize winner for Physics (shared with Pyotr Kapitza and Robert Wilson) "for their discovery of the cosmic microwave background radiation," wrote: "Human wonder at the world around us predates recorded history when the psalmist said: ' What is man that thou art mindful of him?' That was surely not the first time that someone looked up at the heavens and wondered what this world was all about. Archeological evidence—from the crescent moons scratched on the walls on ancient caves to the great blocks at Stonehenge—testifies to our long standing concern with cosmic questions. Astronomy leads us to a unique event, a universe which was created out of nothing, one with the very delicate balance needed to provide exactly the conditions required to permit life, and one which has an underlying supernatural plan. Thus, the observations of modern science seem to lead to the same conclusions as centuries-old intuitions."

Professor Christian Anfinsen of Johns Hopkins University and winner of the 1972 Nobel Prize for Chemistry (shared with Stanford Moore and William Stein) "for their work on ribonuclease, especially concerning the connection between the amino acids sequence and the biologically active conformation," wrote: "Only an idiot can be an atheist. We must admit that there exists an incomprehensible power or force with limitless foresight and knowledge to start the whole universe going in the first place. I enclose a favourite quotation from Einstein that agrees completely with my own point of view: 'The most beautiful and the most profound emotion we can experience is the sensation of the mystical. It is the sower of all true science. That deeply emotional conviction of the presence of a superior reasoning power which is revealed in the incomprehensible universe forms my idea of God.'" Indeed, as the psalmist said: *"The fool hath said in his heart: 'There is no God'"* (Psalm 14:1).

Professor D H R Barton of the University of London, the 1969 Nobel Prize winner for Chemistry, was quite precise. "God is Truth. There is no incompatibility between science and religion. Both are seeking the same truth. Science shows that God exists. Our universe is infinitely large and infinitely small. It is infinite in time past and in future time. We can never understand infinity. It is the ultimate truth, which is God. The observations and experiments of science are so wonderful that the truths that they establish can surely be accepted as another manifestation of God. God shows himself by allowing man to establish truth."

Professor Arthur Shawlow, Nobel Prize winner for Physics in 1981 (shared with Nicholaas Bloembergen and Kai Seighban) "for their contribution to the development of laser spectroscopy," conceded: "It seems to me that when confronted with the marvels of life and the universe, one must ask why and not just how. The only possible answers are religious. I find a need for God in the universe and in my own life. Scientific research is a worshipful act in that it reveals more of the wonder of God's creation. Current research in astrophysics seems to indicate that the ultimate origin of the universe may not be only unknown but unknowable. That is, if we assume the Big Bang occurred, which present evidence strongly supports, there is no real way to find out what came before the Big Bang. It is surely right to pursue as far as possible the scientific understanding of the origins of the universe, but it is probably wrong to think that we have the final answers and that there are no further surprises to come. From a religious point of view, we assume that God did it and hope to find out something about how He did it."

Francis Collins is the Director of the US National Human Genome Research Institution, which co-mapped the 3 billion biochemical letters of our genetic blueprint. He is a forthright Christian, who converted from atheism at age 27. He claims, like Louis Pasteur, that scientific discoveries bring man closer to God. "When you make a breakthrough," he wrote, "it is a moment of scientific exhilaration because you have been on this search and seem to have found it. But it is also a moment when I at least feel a closeness to the Creator in the sense of having now perceived something that no human knew before but which God knew all along. When you have for the first time in front of you this 3.1 billion letter instruction book that conveys all kinds of information and all kinds of mystery about humankind, you cannot survey that going through page after page without a sense of awe. I cannot help but look at these pages and have a vague sense that this is giving me a glimpse of the mind of God.

"By being outside of nature, God is also outside of space and time. Hence, at the moment of the creation of the universe, God could also have activated evolution with full knowledge of how it would turn out. Evolution is not incompatible with God having designed it. Once life arose, the process of evolution and natural selection permitted the development of a biological diversity and complexity over very long periods of time. But while evolution may explain some features of the moral law, it cannot explain why it should have any real significance. If it is solely an evolutionary convenience, there is really no such thing as good or evil. But for me, it is much more that that. The moral law is a reason to think of God as plausible—not just a God who sets the universe in motion but a God who cares about human beings, because we seem unique amongst creatures on the planet to have this far-developed sense of morality."

Indeed, in my opinion the debate between the atheist and evolutionist Richard Dawkins and Francis Collins is a typical example of the familiar maxim: "A little science takes one away from God but a great deal of science brings one back to Him."

At the same time, Professor Vladamir Prelog of Prague, Czechoslovakia, a Nobel Prize winner for Chemistry in 1975 (shared with John Cornforth) "for research into the stereochemistry of organic molecules and reactions," was amusingly self-critical and philosophic: "Winners of Nobel Prizes are not more competent about God, religion and life after death than other people; some of them like myself are agnostics. They just don't know. Indeed, my agnosticism goes so far that I am not even certain whether I am an agnostic! I am pleased, for instance, by Faust's answer to Gretchen's question. I often cite Max Planck: 'God is at the beginning of every religion and at the end of the natural sciences.' I am also in agreement with the clever rabbi who during a heated symposium on the existence of God said in exasperation, 'Look, God is so great that He does not even need to exist.'"

Finally, when the question was posed to him: "How should science and the scientist approach origin questions, specifically the origin of the universe and the origin of life?" Professor Ragnar Granit of the University of Helsinki, the 1967 winner of the Nobel Prize for Physiology/Medicine (shared with H. Keffer Hartline and George Wald "for their discoveries concerning the primary physiological and chemical visual processes in the eye"), replied briefly and to the point: "Humbly."

# Chapter 6

## THE ORIGIN OF
## INTERNATIONAL TERRORISM

*War becomes difficult when people are willing to die
and use their bodies as a weapon of destruction.*

AIDS was first diagnosed in 1981 but the most recent threat to human life is the emergence of the suicide bomber and international terrorism. On September 11, 2001, in an unprecedented attack on the lives of civilians on American soil, a small group of Muslim terrorists were successful in destroying two famous landmarks in New York. The nation was stunned by what some termed the first war of the 21st century.

They used the most primitive and unsophisticated of weapons to overpower the cockpit crew of three planes and committed suicide while taking over three thousand souls with them. They were also convinced that their reward for this evil was an admission ticket to paradise. It is all part of the legacy of the Palestinian-Israeli conflict and the ensuing emergence of large-scale international killings by Islamic extremists or so-called fundamentalists. It is a form of warfare called "terrorism." It is a new and dangerous worldwide threat to peace, but it has its roots in biblical history.

Terrorism, in the most widely accepted contemporary usage of the term, is fundamentally and inherently political and the use of power to achieve political change. All terrorist acts involve violence or the threat of violence. They are meant to instill fear and thereby intimidate a wide large audience, which might include a rival ethnic or religious group, a national government or political party or public opinion in general. One may therefore define modern-day terrorism as the deliberate creation and exploitation of fear through violence and the logic and justification behind it is that it is the only weapon available to the weak and powerless when confronting a stronger and more powerful opponent.

This is the age of Muslim wars. In fact, history records that Muslims fight each other far more often than do peoples of other civilizations. One of the more recent examples is the civil war between the Fatah party and Hamas in Palestine. When the Muslim wars came to America on September 11, 2001, it revealed the existence of a sizeable terrorist network with cells in perhaps 40 countries and with the expertise and resources to attempt well-planned simultaneous attacks. For the first time the network struck within the United States with devastating effect. Its action also highlighted the likelihood of subsequent attacks with the somewhat more distinct possibility of the use of nuclear weapons, especially mini-nukes. Indeed, throughout the Muslim world, and particularly among Arabs, there exists a great sense of grievance, resentment, envy and hostility toward the West, its religion and its wealth (especially the United States with its support for Israel), power and culture which Islam considers to be degenerate.

For the Islamic fundamentalists in general, no peace or compromise with Israel is possible and any concession is only a step toward the new "final solution"—the dissolution of the state of Israel, the return of the land of Palestine to whom they consider to be its true owners, namely, the Muslim Palestinians, and the departure of the intruders. However, for the followers of Osama bin Laden, the declaration of war against the United States also marks the resumption of the struggle for religious dominance of the world that began in the seventh century. To them, America, a friend of Israel, also exemplifies a civilization, which, like Rome and Byzantium, has become degenerate and demoralized, ready and needed to be overthrown.

It is said that bin Laden once told a relative that "the West has exported to us its corrosive culture. We are exporting something back that corrodes their society. Their society is as wicked as their culture." According to Adam Robinson, bin Laden also once reaffirmed his call for *jihad,* saying: "The Islamic world is facing a period of trouble; we are entering a period of danger. I refer to the presence of Christian forces in Arab lands. The Christians are attempting to establish full control over our region. For the first time since the rise of our Holy Prophet Muhammad, peace be upon him, we see a situation where the sacred places of our religion — the Kabah ( in Mecca), the Nabvi Mosque (in Medina) and the Al Quasa

Mosque (in Jerusalem) are under the open and covert power of non-Muslims. It has now become obligatory for Muslims, wherever they are in the world, to begin to struggle to oust the infidels from our sacred places."

The world is now confronted with the emergence of a new kind of extremist Islamic terrorism, not in keeping with mainstream Islam, and violence, and vengence have now spawned suicidal missions with the indiscriminate killing, frequently of innocent civilians. But war becomes difficult when people are willing to die and use their bodies as a weapon of destruction. It has turned out to be an effective weapon of war. It has now become an ideology; an ideology of fear in this modern-day clash of the civilizations and clash of the religions.

It was national fanaticism which spawned the astonishing campaign of suicidal attacks carried out by Japanese airmen toward the end of World War II. The actions of those men were the blueprint for the suicide bombing, which, in another form, is bringing terror and death to our world more than 50 years later. It was originally proposed calling that movement *shimpu*, a word for "divine wind." However, another word of much the same meaning soon made its way into the vernacular of World War II—*kamikaze*. It was the Allies' most terrifying enemy and mixed with fear was revulsion at the way that Japan had turned suicide into a weapon of death. Between October 1944 and August 1945, 3913 *kamikaze* pilots were known to have died in those suicide missions against the US Navy, their enemy. However, today's Islamic fundamentalist suicide bombers do not distinguish civilians from enemies. Like the Japanese, however, they too expect a "divine" reward.

As Emma Williams wrote in *The Spectator* of 17 May, 2003: "Living in Jerusalem has meant living Israeli fear: the fear of taking children to school and hearing a suicide bomber detonating himself outside the school gates; of not wanting to go to a restaurant or bar or coffee shop for fear of being blown up; of hesitating to call Israeli friends for fear that one of their children had been killed in the latest Palestinian terrorist atrocity. On the other hand, it is impossible to believe that any Israelis who visit the Occupied Territories and see the pitiful state of the lives of the Palestinians—perpetually under curfew, humiliated at checkpoints by perceived to be arrogant Israelis— would not choke in revulsion.

"And so, people are now afraid and there is a pervading atmosphere of terror in many countries. Whereas it was once restricted to Israel and the Lebanon, it has now grown into a global threat. Moreover today's weapons of mass destruction, including biological and chemical weapons, are becoming increasingly available to more states, and what is more frightening, to small groups and even individuals. The great fear of the post-World War II years was of nuclear weapons. The fear now is that some countries, forced to choose between defeat and the use of nuclear weapons, might just opt for the latter and that even if they have to 'go down' with it, at least they will take others with them."

Apropos this, Mao tse-Tung is said to have once remarked that a nuclear war resulting in hundreds of millions of victims might be worthwhile if it brought about the final demise of capitalism and the dominance of the Communist world. Joseph Stalin, expressing a total disregard for the sanctity of life, is also reputed to have said: "A single death is a tragedy; a million is a statistic."

As Walter Laquer wrote in his book *The New Terrorism*: "The real innovation in the late twentieth century is the appearance of radical quasi-religious national groups, adopting terrorism as their main form of struggle, sometimes within the framework of established religion and sometimes in the form of millenarian sects. Fanaticism inspired by all kinds of religious-sectarian-nationalistic convictions is now taking on a millenarian and apocalyptic tone. We are witnessing the emergence of new kinds of terrorist violence, based on quasi-religious beliefs. It was once believed that the horrific consequences of using weapons of mass destruction will be a deterrent to war. Now we know that rage, anger and fanaticism are such powerful emotions that in some societies mass destruction is no more of a deterrent than self-destruction."

# Chapter 7

## WHOSE PALESTINE IS IT?

*This land is mine.*

Its roots are in biblical history and unless we are well-versed in chapters 15-22 of *The Book of Genesis*, we cannot truly understand what the Israeli-Palestinian problem is all about or be able to appreciate the central question: "Whose Palestine is it?"

Middle Eastern history really begins with Abraham around 2000 BC. According to the Old Testament, Abraham's wife Sarai (Sarah) was childless when the Lord said to him: *"Fear not, Abram (Abraham), I will protect you and reward you greatly for your righteousness." Abraham then said: "Lord God, what is my reward? I still have no child of my own. Eliezer of Damascus is the steward of my household. Should he be my heir?" "He shall not be your heir; your heir shall be your flesh and blood,"* answered the Lord. *Then taking him outside, he said to Abraham: "Look up to the heavens and count the stars if you can. Such will be your descendants"* (Genesis 15: 1-6).

However, throughout the whole of 11 years Abraham's wife Sarah still remained childless and one day, growing impatient for the birth of the promised son and not understanding the divine delay, she said to Abraham: *"The Lord has not let me have a child. Go to my handmaid Hagar. Take her to yourself; in that way I may have a child through her."* Hagar was an Egyptian maidservant and in those days it was not unusual for a man to have more than one wife nor for a wife to give her handmaid to her husband. And so, childless women like Sarah would sometimes ask their husbands to produce children through a *trusted* handmaid and the wife would be thought of as the mother of the handmaid's children.

Abraham was 86 years old when Hagar conceived, however, once she conceived, contrary to custom, her mistress was despised in her eyes and Hagar treated her with contempt. Mutual jealously then led to Hagar's running away from the house after Sarah dealt harshly with her (Genesis 16:4-6). Hagar was then told by the angel of the Lord: *"Return to your mistress and submit to her. I will so greatly multiply your offspring that they can be counted for a multitude. Now you have conceived, and you will bear a son; you shall name him Ishmael for the Lord has heard your cry of distress. A wild-ass of a man he would be, with his hand against everyone and everyone's hand against him, and he shall live at odds with all his kin"* (Genesis 16:9-12). Now, to those who believe the Old Testament text to be prophetic, unfortunately this historic biblical image of Ishmael, the father of the Arabs, is now thought to be reinforced by the Arab Muslim wars and present-day terrorism.

Abraham was 100 years when his legitimate wife Sarah, long past the age when she might have a child, eventually bore him a son Isaac, as Yahweh had promised. The jealousies then deepened and Sarah sent away Hagar and her son Ishmael. After much suffering Hagar went through the desert to Paran and then returned to Egypt where as the years went by she got a wife for Ishmael (Genesis 21:1-21). According to the Bible, Ishmael "set himself to defy his brothers." The Qu'ran teaches that he went to Mecca, and his descendants who grew up in Arabia are the Muslims whereas those of Isaac, who remained in Palestine were the Jews. That Jews and Arabs are "cousins," who were descended from Isaac and Ishmael respectively, is accepted in both Jewish and Islamic writings. Indeed, it is written that at the death of Abraham, his sons Isaac and Ishmael buried him in the cave of Machpelah (Genesis 25:9-10). As Prime Minister Shimon Peres once said in a 1985 address to the United Nations General Assembly: "The sons of Abraham will have become quarrelsome, but remain family nonetheless."

But according to the Old Testament, God made certain promises to Abraham regarding Ishmael and Isaac: *"And as for Ishmael, I have heard thee: Behold, I have blessed him and will make him fruitful, and will multiply him exceedingly; twelve princes shall he beget and I will make him a great nation. But my covenant I will establish with Isaac"* (Genesis 17:20-21). In fact, in the New Testament, Paul, in his letter to the Galatians, wrote: "Does not the Scripture say: 'Cast out the handmaid and her son: This son of the handmaid shall not inherit with the son of the free woman' " (Galatians 4:30). In short, Paul asserts that as Ishmael was not considered to be the legitimate son of Abraham, God gave the land of Palestine to Abraham and his seed through Isaac, son of Sarah, and then to Isaac's son, Jacob: *"I am the God of your father, the God of Abraham, the God of Isaac and the God of Jacob," Yahweh said to Moses* (Exodus 3:6).

The Qu'ran, on the other hand, written centuries upon centuries after the Old Testament and New Testament scripts, directly contradicts this. From the Muslim point of view, the Jewish revelation in the Old Testament was a divine revelation that was corrupted. Islam states that Abraham's first son was Ishmael and that Isaac was born afterwards as a reward to him for his obedience to God's command to sacrifice Ishmael and not Isaac. And so, the Qu'ran insists that Ishmael was "the son of the promise" (covenant) and not Isaac as is written in the Jewish and Christian Scriptures. This is a very important contention, one of which must be wrong, *very* wrong.

Now, following the call from Yahweh, Abraham and his descendants left for the land of Canaan (Palestine) but in time the Pharaohs enslaved them in Egypt. Around 1200 BC, Moses then led the Hebrews out of Egypt and they wandered in the Sinai desert. According to the Bible, the Hebrews at the time of the giving of the Law at Mt. Sinai numbered more than 600,000. Centuries later King David (1010-975 BC) eventually captured Jerusalem, after which it was called the City of David. After a colourful history of conquests and reconquests, in the 7th century AD Islam conquered Jerusalem but the Muslim conquerors were eventually ejected by the Crusaders in 1099.

That first Christian Crusade (1096-99) was spectacularly successful and captured Jerusalem on 15 July, 1099. A second Crusade (1145-49) was carefully prepared but a new leader of Islam, Salah ad-Din (or Saladin), annihilated the army of the Crusaders and captured the Holy City. A third Crusade (1188-1192) eventually ended in a truce between Richard the Lionheart of England and Saladin. Through the Ottoman Turks, the Muslims again held Jerusalem, and the Holy City would not come under Western control again until the end of World War I when General Edmond Allenby and his British troops captured it from the Turks and set the stage for the reestablishment of a Jewish nation and state.

Indeed, throughout all the centuries of their exile, from the farthest corners of the Earth Jews have prayed for their return to Jerusalem: "Next year in Jerusalem!" History has no parallel to this mystic bond. All through a succession of conquerors and rulers from King David who captured it in 1010 BC, how often has Jerusalem been pagan, Christian or Muslim? How many different conquerors have wielded their power over it? —Jebusites, Egyptians, Babylonians, Persians, Greeks, Romans, Muslim Arabs, Seljuks, Fatimids, Crusaders, Mamelukes, Ottoman Turks, British, Jordanians, and now again, the Israelites. For close to 3,000 years, the Jews did not have a country of their own. However, they survived those 3,000 years and preserved their ethnic identity among alien cultures.

Not until Zionism evolved as a movement in the 19th century, largely in reaction to pogroms in Russia, did significant numbers of European Jews begin to migrate to Ottoman-controlled Palestine and by 1845, Jews formed the largest single community in Jerusalem, the vanguard of an influx that gathered momentum after Great Britain endorsed the creation of a Jewish homeland through the Balfour Declaration of 1917. The migration gained added urgency when Hitler came to power, promulgated anti-Jewish laws in the 1930s, rounded up all the Jews in Germany, deported them to concentration camps and exterminated an estimated 6 million of them in gas chambers with hydrogen cyanide or Zyklon B. However, out of the Holocaust grew the international compassion for the proposal of a new Israel as a sanctuary for the Jews and the historic decision by the United Nations General Assembly in November 1947 to partition Palestine was passed by a vote of thirty three in favour, thirteen against, and ten in abstention.

Now, those Jews, who rely on the biblical deed to the land and claim that "this land is mine," take their history from the ancient period of 4,000 years or so ago, skipping over the centuries of Muslim rule that followed. On the other hand, those Arabs who regard history as their ally, tend to begin with the Muslim conquest of Jerusalem in the 7th century AD, blithely ignoring the Jewish kingdom set up by David that existed there 2,000 years before Muhammad was born. However, as one author concluded: "It is clear from the Scriptures that whatever claims the Arabs—and the Palestinian Arabs in particular—may make upon the Holy Land, those claims will have to be based upon political, historical or practical grounds and not upon Scripture, and as far as the Word of God says in the Hebrew Old Testament, the land has been specifically promised as an everlasting possession to the descendants of Abraham through Isaac and then Jacob."

In his book *The Palestinians,* published in the late 1970s, Jonathan Dimbleby, the British television reporter, gave a history of the Middle East from a Palestinian point of view. In defense of the plight of the Palestinians, he wrote: "The Palestinian will fight Israel, and he will do so, if not with a gun, then with a bomb. The Israeli soldiers will seek to kill him. If they succeed, they will report that another 'terrorist' has been eliminated. And the Palestine Liberation Organization (PLO) will announce that another 'martyr' has been born... It is now generally agreed that the conflict in the Middle East is, at root, a territorial dispute between two peoples, the Israelis and the Palestinians. The Zionist case for Palestine is well known. The Palestinian case is equally powerful, though it is still referred to in terms which reflect the imbalance of our Western perception, as the 'Palestinian problem.' This book is neither a hymn to terrorism nor an apologia for the PLO. It is, however, an attempt to redress our imbalance of perception... The most obvious symbol of this distortion is the use of the word 'terrorist' to distinguish Palestinian from Israeli atrocities. 'Terrorists' do not have jet planes to mutilate innocents from a distance; they do it with bombs in markets. Is the former less heinous than the latter because it is sanctioned by an Israeli Cabinet? But again and again the Israeli authorities emerge morally inviolate from their military adventures while the PLO is compared to the Nazis or the Ku Klux Klan for refusing to give up guerilla war..."

This commentary was written in 1970. Thirty one years later, on September 11, 2001, Arab "terrorists" did indeed use "jet planes to mutilate innocents from a distance" but, to the shock of the world, with suicide bombers! A new type of warfare was born—suicide bombings. And so, time has proven Dimbleby to be wrong! As Samuel T. Huntington, the Albert J. Weatherhead III University professor at Harvard, wrote in the lead article for *Newsweek* magazine of December, 2001: "An outbreak of violence is sweeping across the world. What are the root causes and will they erupt into a full-scale global conflict? The makings of a possible 'clash of civilizations' are present. Contemporary global politics is the age of Muslim wars. Muslim wars have replaced the Cold War as the principal form of international conflict. These wars include wars of terrorism, guerilla wars, civil wars and interstate conflicts. These instances of Muslim violence could congeal into one major clash of civilizations between Islam and the West or between Islam and the Rest."

Meanwhile Lance Lambert, writing from a biblical and Israeli point of view in his book *The Uniqueness of Israel,* defended the Israeli claim to the land. He argued: "For the Jews it is the country of the patriarchs. It is the country of Moses and Joshua. It is the land where kings ruled from the country of David and Solomon. It is the land of the Psalmist. It is a unique land and is the subject of a divine promise. Indeed, no other land on Earth has ever been promised by God to one particular people. It is supposed to be the legacy given to the seed of Abraham, the father of the Jews and the Arabs. Scarcely more than a dot on the map in the Middle East, surrounded by enemies with large territories, it is scarred and coveted by both the Jews and Arabs, who now face each other in a family feud, for the Jews and Arabs are cousins. About 3.5 million Jews and 2 million Arabs live in Israel, but both peoples are victims. Each has suffered at the hands of outsiders, and each has been wounded by the other."

Winston Churchill's history of *The Second World War*, written in 1957, will remain the definitive work on that war. Referring to the Middle East problem, he wrote: "The most intractable of all the difficulties that faced Britain in these regions was Palestine. Ever since the Balfour Declaration of 1917, as a mandatory power Great Britain was confronted with the tortuous problem of combining Jewish immigration to their national home and safeguarding the rights of the Arab inhabitants. Few of us could blame the Jewish people for their violent views on the subject. A race that has suffered the virtual extermination of its nation's existence cannot be expected to be entirely reasonable. The infective violence of the birth of the state of Israel has sharpened the difficulties of the Middle East ever since but the outlook is somber. The position of the hundreds of thousands of Arabs driven from their homes and existing precariously in the no-man's-land created round Israel's frontiers is cruel and dangerous. One thing is clear. Both honour and wisdom demanded that the state of Israel should be preserved, and that this brave, dynamic and complex race should be allowed to live in peace with its neighbours."

But as David Shipler lamented in his book *Arab and Jew*: "I am neither Arab nor Jew. By culture and creed, I should suffer neither pain nor passion over the causes and battles that entangle the two peoples... And yet I cannot help caring... At times a rush of anger would propel me to the conviction that, in their mutual hatreds, both sides deserve each other. And then at other moments I was enveloped by a sense that both sides were right. But I offer no solutions to the problem. I have no prescriptions for peace..." Ariel Sharon also once said in an interview in *Newsweek* of December 17, 2001: "There are problems to which there are no answers: the question of Jerusalem. I believe Jerusalem is the capital of the Jewish people and the capital of the State of Israel, united and undivided forever. Of course, the Palestinians do not accept that." And so, what is the solution to the problem?

But Israel is now threatened more than ever with extinction by its enemies, particularly Iran. However, it was Menachem Begin, more than any other Israeli leader, who saw contemporary events through the prism of the genocide that had been practiced against the Jews. When he ordered Iraq's nuclear reactor bombed, he did so citing the potential for another attempt to exterminate the Jews, and he made that vow of resolution: "Never again."

# THE END OF THIS ERA

# Chapter 8

## THE AIDS VIRUS: A MICROSCOPIC TERRORIST

*Still rapidly growing, the AIDS pandemic is reversing development gains widening the gap between rich and poor, and undermining social and economic security.*

Animals were created before humankind; so were bacteria and viruses. In fact, it is believed that bacteria were already well established on Earth some 3.5 billion years ago. Viruses are much simpler and are the smallest known infectious agents, approximately a hundred times smaller than bacteria. Unlike bacteria, viruses reproduce only within cells and borrow (probably a more appropriate word is "hijack") the genetic apparatus of the cells which they invade. Viruses do this extremely efficiently, turning a bacterium, for example, into a factory for making viruses. In some cases it takes no more than ten minutes for a bacterium infected with a single virus to produce a hundred new viral particles. However, I was unable to ascertain with any certainty from the literature when viruses first evolved. And so, the origin of viruses is still an open question. All that can be conjectured is that because viruses are totally parasitic, there must have been cells before there were viruses.

As Graig Venter, the co-discoverer of the human genome, once said: "We have identified more microbes in our guts than the 100 trillion human cells that we have in our bodies. We have also catalogued the tens of thousands of microbes and viruses that are in the air we constantly breathe. These modern tools of genomics are rapidly revealing to us the incredible world of microbes that we exist within and exists within us."

We forget, for example, that an influenza virus was the cause of the so-called "Spanish flu" pandemic, which appeared towards the end of World War I. It killed more people in a shorter period of time than did all the weapons of World War I, which caused ten million deaths over a four-year period. Crossing national barriers, the virus infected some one billion people and claimed more than twenty million lives in less than a single year. In fact, various influenza viruses kill more than 500,000 people every year.

The current AIDS pandemic is a grim reminder that these infinitesimally small viruses and bacteria, older than mankind, are sturdier than man and are also some of our deadliest enemies. In fact, they were able to survive the inhospitable and hot environment of early creation times. Indeed, one of the greatest threats to human life in today's world is the virus of AIDS. The human immunodeficiency virus (HIV) replicates very rapidly and as many as 10 billion new viruses are produced each day in the blood as opposed to the daily production of one billion human white blood cells, which attempt to ward off the viral infection. With this tenfold numerical advantage the virus eventually overwhelms our immune defense force.

Since researchers first identified the acquired immunodeficiency syndrome in 1981, more than 30 million people around the world have died from AIDS and an estimated 40 million or more are living with HIV today. In short, the pandemic has already killed more people than all the persons killed in the major world wars of the last century and also exceeds the toll taken by the bubonic plague in Europe in 1347. Still rapidly growing, the pandemic is reversing development gains, widening the gap between rich and poor, and undermining social and economic security. Tens of millions of children and young people are at the front line of the pandemic's advance, bearing the brunt of its impact. Typically, half of all those with HIV become infected before they celebrate their 25th birthday and many of them die from AIDS before they turn 35, leaving behind a generation of children to be raised by grandparents or siblings, most of whom have no economic base.

In fact, one of the major social disruptions and consequences of HIV/AIDS is the fragmentation of the family unit. It also has very important negative offshoots of a spiritual nature in homes where there are no parents and certain parts of the world are fast becoming one huge orphanage. No other infectious disease of the modern era has had such a devastating impact on the world's youngest and most vulnerable citizens.

But the virus of AIDS, while responsible for the disease, is not *per se* the cause of the worldwide pandemic and HIV would be still unknown were it not for the fact that mankind through the sexual revolution, which heightened in the sixties with the ever increasing promotion and proclivity of sexual promiscuity worldwide, has created the morally unhealthy environment, which is a fertile soil for HIV's survival, growth and multiplication. This has catapulted the virus from obscurity in the distant past to the present-day worldwide high prevalence. Meanwhile, so-called "safe sex" through condom usage is being continually touted as the answer to the spread of HIV/AIDS. However, in spite of (if not because of) the widespread advertisements and promotion of condoms, the yearly incidence of HIV infections continues to increase. And so, the two thriving businesses in today's world are condom factories and funeral agencies!

AIDS and terrorism are two of today's major threats to life and we are therefore living in a world of terror at both the macroscopic and microscopic levels of human life. There are many uncanny similarities. In the Arab world of Islamic fundamentalism, the assassination of political leaders is one strategy, which is used by some extremists to attain certain desired outcomes. In like manner, the virus of AIDS seeks and kills the so-called "leaders" or "generals" of the body's immunological defense force, the CD4 white cells (lymphocytes), which orchestrate and summon different specialized cells in the defense of the body whenever there is an invading organism. Because of this selective destruction of the CD4 cells, the body's immune defense force does not spring into action and remains, as it were, in their barracks thus making ineffective our personal homeland security system.

Now, deoxyribonucleic acid (DNA) is classically referred to as "the code of life" and is found in every human cell. Viruses are simply small pieces of DNA or ribonucleic acid (RNA). Ironically, however, these DNA and RNA viruses are also capable of destroying human life. Indeed, the virus of AIDS may be dubbed "a biological weapon of mass destruction" and can therefore be labeled a "microscopic terrorist." Terrorists indulge in kidnapping as a tool of warfare and for the exchange of prisoners. The virus of AIDS may also be considered to be a kidnapper of our white CD4 cells and uses them for the production of new viral recruits.

The similarity does not stop there. After the virus attaches itself to and invades the CD4 lymphocyte, it takes over the cell's command centre, as it were, and instructs it to make copies of itself (10 billion new virions a day). In the process, the lymphocyte literally "explodes," spewing and freeing new viral "terrorists" and viral "clones" into the blood stream to continue the cycle of terror, havoc and death. This is the "microscopic world of terrorism" with the destruction each day of billions of our "life-protecting" lymphocytes, which come to our defense and protection. In like manner, the suicide bomber "explodes" himself causing terror, havoc and death.

There are eight different clades or subtypes of the virus in different parts of the world and similarly there are several different terrorist cells in various countries of the world sometimes using different tactics, but, like the AIDS virus, with one common purpose—to destroy life. There is yet another parallel. In the treatment of HIV/AIDS, altered versions or analogues of certain subunits of DNA called nucleosides, which prevent the replication of the virus, are now used as treatment to prolong lives. They are called antiretroviral drugs. These nucleoside analogues are also colloquially called in the world of retrovirology, the "nukes." Paradoxically, the word "nukes" is also an abbreviation for "nuclear" weapons of mass destruction, which are a threat to the survival and replication of all living species.

Whereas the AIDS virus and its multiplication may be kept at bay with antiretroviral drugs, many of these viruses lie dormant in what are called in the scientific literature "hidden sanctuaries or cells," such as lymph nodes, but they promptly resurge and multiply with full force when the treatment process is interrupted or stopped. Coincidentally also, the terminology used in the literature for places where terrorists bide their time and hide before being re-activated is "sanctuaries" or "sleeper cells." The virus of AIDS also frequently changes its outer protein coat and becomes unrecognizable by its victim's immune surveillance system. In like manner, the suicide bomber sometimes "changes his/her outer coat," as it were, puts on a disguise and becomes unrecognizable.

In short, the microscopic world is in nefarious union with the macroscopic in this total warfare and cult of death in today's world.

# Chapter 9

## THE MAYANS, AZTECS,
## AND
## OUR LADY OF GUADALUPE

*Am I not here, I who am your Mother?*

Long before the birth of Christ, the central and southern regions of Mexico were inhabited by people thought to be descendants of primitive nomads, who had reached a high degree of civilization. Of singular importance were the Olmecs from about 2000 BC to 200 AD, then the ancient Maya civilization, which reached its peak around 300-800 AD. Classic Maya civilization collapsed for reasons still unknown between 800-900 AD and to this day no one can verify where they went. Then there were the Toltecs (900-1170 AD). Before those dates we only have vague semi-historical data on the events which took place in the Valley of Mexico.

Graham Hancock's book *Fingerprints of the Gods* fascinated me. A review of this best-seller says: "As we recover the truth about prehistory, and discover the real meaning of ancient myths and monuments, it becomes apparent that a warning has been handed down to us, a warning of a terrible cataclysm that affects the Earth in great cycles at irregular intervals of time—a cataclysm that may be about to recur."

As Hancock wrote, the Mayans, justifiably regarded as the greatest ancient civilization to have arisen in the New World, were gifted with an inexplicably advanced state of astro-calendrical and mathematical knowledge. For example, the use of zero was used by the Mayans 900 years before the Arabs introduced it in Europe. Perhaps it was a knowledge that they had inherited from an older and wiser civilization, say, the Olmecs (a thousand years earlier). The question would then be, from where did the Olmecs get it?

The Gregorian calendar was introduced in Europe in 1582 and was based on the best scientific knowledge then available. This is the most widely used calendar in the world today and was decreed by Pope Gregory XIII after whom it was named on 24 February 1582 by papal bull *Inter gravissimas*. It replaced the Julian calendar, which was previously introduced by Julius Caesar in 46 BC, and computed the period of the Earth's orbit around the Sun at 365.25 days. In fact, the Julian calendar was accurate only to about ± seven years and so using this calendar, the millennium could really be anywhere between 1993 and 2007. However, Pope Gregory XIII's reform in 1582 substituted a finer and more accurate calculation—365.2425 days, a difference of .00079 of a day! Scientific advances since 1582 now give the exact length of the solar year to be 365.2422 days.

Strangely and inexplicably enough, the Mayan calendar (between 300 and 800 AD) had previously achieved even greater accuracy and had calculated the solar year to be 365.2420 days, a minor error of only 0.0002 of a day. Similarly, the Mayans revealed a time taken by the Moon to orbit the Earth. Their estimate of this period was 29.528395 days, which is extremely close to the true figure of 29.50588 days computed by the finest modern methods. The Mayan priests also had very accurate tables for the prediction of solar and lunar eclipses.

According to the Mayans, the universe operated in great cycles of approximately 5200 years and their civilization was in the fifth cycle of the Sun. The four other great civilizations before them that were destroyed by great natural disasters. Their current world cycle began on a Mayan date of zero corresponding to 13 August, 3114 BC in our own calendar. We are supposed to be living in the era of the "fifth sun" or cycle, which is calculated to end in *December 2012*. This time we are now in is what has been called among other things, "the end of this creation," and "the end of time, as we know it," and the sixth cycle will begin in 2012. They also believed that these cycles coincided with our spiritual and collective consciousness.

Now, around 1200 AD, somewhere to the northwest of present-day Mexico City, a band of men, women and children abandoned their ancestral homeland Aztlan from which the name Aztec was derived. It was not until much later that these assumed the name "Mexica." Teotihuacan is 50 kilometers northeast of Mexico City. Here you will find the great pyramids—the Pyramid of the Sun, the Pyramid of the Moon and the Pyramid of Quetzalcoatl. According to

Graham Hancock, a complex mathematical relationship appears to exist among the main structures lined up along the so-called "Street of the Dead," which is now a major tourist attraction in Mexico City today. This relationship suggested something extraordinary, namely, that Teotihuacan might originally have been designed as a precise scale model of the solar system. If the centre line of the Pyramid of Quetzalcoatl were taken as denoting the position of the Sun.

Archaeo-astronomers, making use of the latest star-mapping computer programs, had also demonstrated that the three world famous pyramids on Egypt's Giza plateau formed an exact terrestrial diagram of the three belt stars in the constellation of Orion. At Giza, the summits of the Great Pyramid and the Pyramid of Khafre were level, even though the former was a taller building than the latter. Likewise, at Teotihuacan, the summits of the Pyramids of the Sun and the Moon were level even though the former was taller. As Hancock noted, the reason was the same in both cases: the Great Pyramid was built on lower ground than the Pyramid of Khafre, and the Pyramid of the Sun on lower ground than the Pyramid of the Moon. He questioned whether all this could be coincidence and was it not more logical to conclude that there was an ancient connection between Mexico and Egypt? But what was that connection?

But who were the brilliant architects, stone masons, surveyors and engineers who had created the great pyramids? There is no known mechanism that could have manoeuvred such immense blocks into position. There was no technology known to have been available to the ancient Egyptians and the peoples in the Yucatan peninsula capable of achieving such results. One theory was that the pyramid builders could only have been men of great stature (giants). But what has happened to them? Were they destroyed like the dinosaurs? One answer may be that a cataclysm of some kind, a planetary disaster capable of wiping out almost all physical traces of a large civilization, left no records behind.

Now, the Aztecs, like the Mayans (but with slight differences), also believed that the universe operated in great cycles or "suns" and that there had been four such "suns" since the creation of the human race. At the time of the conquest of Mexico in 1529, it was the "fifth sun" that prevailed. According to the rare collection of Aztec documents known as the *Vaticano-Latin Codex*, the "first sun" had a duration of 4008 years. In this age lived the giants. It was destroyed by water. (Note that in the Hebrew Old Testament, Genesis 6:4 states that "at the time the Nephelim (giants) appeared on earth"). The Earth was repopulated and the "second sun" had a duration of 4010 years. During the "second sun," the human race was once more destroyed by high winds and hurricanes. The "third sun" had a duration of 4081 years and was destroyed by fire and then a great Flood involved the entire Earth in the period of the "fourth sun," which had a duration of 5026 years.

The Aztecs considered themselves the "People of the Sun" and believed that to prevent another destruction of the world, which had already occurred four times in the past, the Sun god had to be appeased with a steady diet of human hearts and blood, and human sacrifice was practiced on a scale never before recorded in human history. It has been described by some historians as Satan's empire. Indeed, it had been established that the number of sacrificed victims in the Aztec empire as a whole had risen to about 250,000 a year by the beginning of the 16th century when Hernan Cortes sailed into the Yucatan peninsula.

On arriving in Tenochtitlan, the Spaniards were deeply surprised and impressed by the beauty, order, and cleanliness of this city of between 150,000 to 300,000 inhabitants, one of the largest metropoles in the world at the time. To quote the writing of Cortes himself: "This great city of Tenochtitlan is built on a salt lake. The city itself is as big as Seville or Cordoba. The main streets are very wide and very straight... Among the temples there is one, the principal one, whose great size and magnificence no human tongue could describe... There are as many as forty towers, all of which are so high that, in the case of the largest, there are fifty steps leading up to the main part of it, and the most important of these towers is higher than that of the Cathedral of Seville.'

Almost two years after Cortes entered the pagan Aztec empire of Montezuma, it collapsed and he immediately set out to rebuild the capital city Tenochtitlan. A year later in 1522, he became governor and captain-general of "New Spain," the new name given to the Aztec empire that was. He demanded that the Aztecs convert to Christianity and ordered an end to human sacrifice and cannibalism everywhere. The Spanish monks, who arrived later, succeeded in winning many of the people to the faith and hundreds of thousands were baptized but in certain areas resistance to Christianity lasted for many years. Enter an "apparition."

After most of Old World Europe had become Protestant following the breaking of ties with the Roman Catholic Church by Martin Luther (1480-1546), Huldreich Zwingli (1484-1531), and Jean Calvin (1509-1564), it was on a hill in Tepeyac in what is now called Mexico City and where the Aztecs had once built a temple to the pagan mother-goddess Tonantzin, that she, who called herself the "Mother of the *true* God," appeared for the first time in the New World to an Aztec convert to Christianity, Juan Diego. The year was 1531, ten years after the conquest of Tenochtitlan (now Mexico City).

Very early on Saturday morning, December 9, at that time the feast of the Immaculate Conception, a humble 57-year-old Aztec whose former name was Cuahatlatotzin, meaning "He who speaks like an eagle," and whose new Christian name was Juan Diego, was on his way to Mass on that great feast day of Mary. As he drew near to the little hill of Tepeyac day was beginning to dawn. Much to his amazement, he heard singing on the hill. It was the singing of many birds and their songs, extremely soft and melodious, surpassed that of the coyoltot, the tzinitzcan, and all the other precious birds of Mexico.

He looked towards the hilltop, towards the easterly direction from which the Sun was rising and from where the heavenly singing was coming. Suddenly the singing stopped. Then he heard someone affectionately calling to him from afar: "Juanito, Juan Diegoito," using the diminutive form of his name. He ventured in the direction of the voice and when he had reached the top of the hill, he saw a brilliant white cloud surrounded by the arc of a rainbow, formed by rays of dazzling light streaming from the cloud. A young lady of exquisite beauty, seemingly about 14 years old, then appeared in front of the cloud. The Sun was not yet above the horizon, but when Juan saw her, her clothes were shining as bright as the Sun with golden beams that rayed around her from head to foot. Indeed, so gloriously bright was she that her radiance seemed to turn rocks into pendants of jewels, cactus leaves into emeralds, and their trunks and their thorns shone like gold.

She came from the east and arrived early in the morning when it was beginning to dawn. She appeared as bright as the Sun. But the Sun is a star. She therefore appeared as one of her Marian titles, the Morning Star! Solomon's *Song of Songs* 6:10 was depicted by this apparition: "Who is she that comes forth as the morning star, fair as the moon, bright as the sun, terrible as an army set in battle array." Indeed, she came forth to do battle with Satan on his turf, and Juan Diego was her first Aztec convert and warrior.

She beckoned him to approach her and when he reached the spot where she was, he was filled with wonder as her perfect grandeur surpassed all imagination. He instinctively prostrated himself before her. It was then that she identified herself: "Know for certain, my dearest and youngest son, that I am the perfect and perpetual Virgin Mary, Mother of the *true* God, through whom everything lives, the Lord of all things, who is Master of creation and of Heaven and Earth. I ardently desire that a temple be built here for me where I will show and offer all my love, my compassion, my help, and my protection to the people. I am your merciful mother, the mother of all who live united in this land, and of all mankind, of all those who love me, of those who cry to me, of those who seek me, of those who have confidence in me. Here I will hear their weeping, their sorrow, and their misfortunes. Therefore, in order that my intentions be made known, you must go to the house of the bishop of Mexico city and tell him that I sent you and that it is my desire to have a temple built here..." Juan Diego replied: "My Lady, my child, I am going right away to carry your venerable word. I take my leave of you for the moment, I, your poor Indian."

Now, Juan called her "my child" and in similar fashion the Virgin called him Juanito ( little Juan) and Diegoito (little Diego). As I discovered in my research, it is because reverential diminutives were frequently used in the Nahuatl language. The well-bred person, for example, did not say "your house" but "your little house." This had nothing to do with actual size but was an expression of reverence and endearment. I could not also help being deeply touched and, of course, amused at the reverential obedience and humility of Juan Diego. "I, your poor Indian!"

However, understandably so, Bishop Juan de Zumarraga did not believe Juan Diego's message and very politely dismissed him. At the end of the day Juan returned to the little hilltop where the "Mother of the *true* God" was waiting for him at the very spot where she had appeared the first time. He then respectfully pleaded: "I beg you, my lady, my queen, my little one, to entrust one of the nobles to bear your kind breath, your kind word: someone who is held in esteem, someone who is known, respected, and honoured in order that he might be believed, because I am really just a man of the field. The place in which you sent me is a place where I am unaccustomed to going or spending any time. My youngest daughter, my lady, my little one, please forgive me…"

"The perfect and perpetual Virgin" listened to his plea with great sympathy and understanding, but implored him to go again to see the bishop on the morrow: "Tell him it is I, the ever Virgin Mary: I, who am the Mother of God, who sends you." Juan obeyed and returned to the bishop. This time the bishop was more impressed, but he told him that the lady must provide some proof that she was really the Mother of God. It was a reasonable reaction, in my opinion.

At sunset Juan Diego was back on the hill of Tepeyac where the lady was waiting for him and she assured him that on the following day she would give him the sign which the bishop had requested. He then went home to rest. However, when he reached home that evening, he found his uncle Juan Bernardino extremely ill and rather than returning to Tepeyac, he spent the whole day caring for his uncle. During that night, Juan Bernardino thought that he was going to die and asked his nephew to go to Tenochtitlan to bring back a priest to anoint him.

The following morning, very concerned about his beloved uncle, Juan Diego set out on a different route around the hill of Tepeyac so that the lady, if she was there, would not detain him from his mission. However, she came down the side of the hill and intercepted him. Embarrassed and distressed that he had not kept his promise to her, he prostrated himself and greeted her with these words which must have amused her: "My young lady, youngest of my children, my child, I hope that you are happy. How are you this morning? Are you in good humor and health this morning, my lady, my little one?" With this flattery, he then told her about the plight of his uncle.

When Juan Diego's tale came to an end, the "merciful mother" consoled him: "Listen, do not be afraid or troubled with grief. Do not fear any illness or vexation, anxiety or pain. Am I not here, I who am your mother? Are you not under my shadow and protection?

Am I not the cause of your joy? Are you not in the folds of my mantle? In the crossing of my arms? What more do you need?" She paused for a while, and with a maternal and sympathetic smile, she gently added: "Do not let your uncle's illness worry you because he is not going to die. Be assured that he is already well." As was later discovered, at that very moment Juan Bernardino recovered.

She then told Juan Diego to climb up the hill and that there he would find flowers in bloom which he should pluck and bring back to her. Juan climbed the hill with great alacrity and renewed vigour, and on reaching the hill-crest, his eyes opened in wonderment. There on the hill was a brilliant profusion of flowers. They were Castilian (Spanish) roses of exquisite fragrance, fresh and glittering with dewdrops. Not only were they in bloom out of season, but it would have been impossible for any flowers to grow in such a stony terrain, which could  only yield thistles and cactus plants. Spreading out his tilma like an apron, he filled it with the colourful blooms, and with great joy he descended to where she was waiting for him. She then gave a feminine touch to the miraculous bouquet and carefully rearranged the flowers with her own hands, saying as she did so: "My youngest and dearest son, these flowers are the proof, the sign that you are to take to the bishop... You will be my ambassador fully worthy of my confidence... Tell him everything... Tell him once again all that you have seen and heard here..."

Juan Diego then returned to the bishop's house, opened his folded tilma and exposed the bouquet of roses arranged *a la Maria*. They were Spanish roses for the Spanish bishop. But they were not just ordinary roses. Warren H. Carroll is the President and Professor of History at Christendom College, USA and a convert to Catholicism since 1968. In his well-researched book *Our Lady of Guadalupe and The Conquest of Darkness*, he wrote: 'When he arrived again at the bishop's house, Juan Diego was kept waiting a long time by the bishop's attendants, who eventually insisted on seeing the roses, but when they tried to take some of them they could not because they became not roses that they could touch, but as if they were painted or embroidered." Indeed, they were mystical roses from the Mystical Rose herself!

But after the roses cascaded to the floor, another and greater shock was in store for Bishop Zumarraga. There upon the tilma was a full portrait of the "Mother of the true God" as Juan Diego had seen her. All the people in the room fell to their knees. Overwhelmed, the bishop, weeping and sorrowful, begged Our Lady's forgiveness for not having complied with her wishes. It was Tuesday, December 12, 1531. Two weeks later, a triumphant procession of Aztecs followed by Franciscan and Dominican missionaries, carried the sacred image to a small makeshift chapel on Tepeyac hill, singing exultantly: "The Virgin is one of us! Our Sovereign Lady is one of us!"

Now, she wore a blue mantle which fell all the way to her feet, speckled all over with golden stars and numerous flowers. Forty six stars were positioned on the right and left flaps of her gown and a crescent Moon was at her feet. In the center of the golden neckline of her gown hung a brooch with a black cross. It was identical to the cross on the banner and helmets of the Spanish conquerors, signaling to the Aztecs that her religion was the same as that of the Spaniards. She wore a blue sash around her waist and the tassels on it signified that she was in a state of maternity. The concave side of the Moon was facing east. Not by coincidence, on that December 12, 1531 there was a crescent Moon in the sky whose concave side faced the east! The Catholic Spaniard clergy then identified her as the Woman of Revelation 12:1-2: *"A great sign appeared in the sky, a woman clothed with the sun, with the moon under her feet, and on her head a crown of twelve stars. Because she was with child, she wailed in pain as she laboured to give birth."*

In May 1979, studies by infrared photography, which can unmask such things as brush strokes and expose the existence of any preliminary drawing underneath (which was an essential prerequisite for nearly all paintings at that time) were undertaken by Dr. Phillip Callahan, a renowned research biophysicist at the University of Florida. He ruled out any brush stroke over-painting or any preliminary drawings by an artist in the body of the image. He concluded that the image on the tilma had qualities of colour and used the weave of the cloth in such a way that the image could not be the work of human hands.

A scientist from the National Aeronautic Space Academy (NASA) also conducted an independent analysis of the tilma and concluded that there is no earthly way to explain the quality of the pigments used for the pink dress, the blue veil, the face or the hands, the permanence of the colours or its vividness after several centuries. In fact, to this date the image cannot be explained by science and has shown no signs of deterioration after 477 years although normally the coarse fabric made from the maguey cactus disintegrates within 20-60 years. Fibers from the tilma were also sent to the 1938 Nobel prize winner Richard Kuhn, then Director of the Chemistry Department of the Kaiser Willhelm Institution (subsequently the Max Planck Institute). He found that the chemicals (paints) used to cover the tilma were neither animal, vegetable, nor mineral dyes and were unknown to science.

More recently, Dr. Enrique Graue, Director of the Ophthalmology Hospital, Nuestra Señora de la Luz in Mexico City, had this to say: "I was dumbfounded. The eyes on the tilma displayed a depth and curvature and reflected light exactly like living eyes. In them were reflected twelve people, who were present in the courtyard on the day Juan Diego opened his cloak, and the amazing fact is that the same figures appeared in both eyes at precisely the positions expected by the law of optics and twin-eyed physiology." Of course, it was not the first time in history that science had to bow to the miraculous!

But science was to be humbled even further. More recently it has been found that the stars seen on the Virgin's mantle corresponded exactly to part of the constellation of stars in the sky that day. This inspired intuition of Fr. Marion Sanchez was arduously researched by Dr. J. Canto Ylla and Dr. Armando Garcia de Leon of the National University of Mexico, who showed that the winter solstice, normally due to occur on December 22, occurred at 10:40 a.m. local time (90 west of Greenwich) on Tuesday, December 12, 1531, the exact day and perhaps the exact time of the actual miracle on the tilma in the presence of Bishop Juan Zumarraga. It was the sky of the winter solstice at 19 degrees latitude, the geographical correspondent of present-day Mexico City (see Fig. 4).

This tilma of 1531 still exists today for the entire world to see in the Basilica of Our Lady of Guadalupe in Mexico City. As Bishop Renfrew from Scotland once said: "Those (supernatural) mysteries level us all, the brainy and the brainless, for they save us from self esteem and pride."

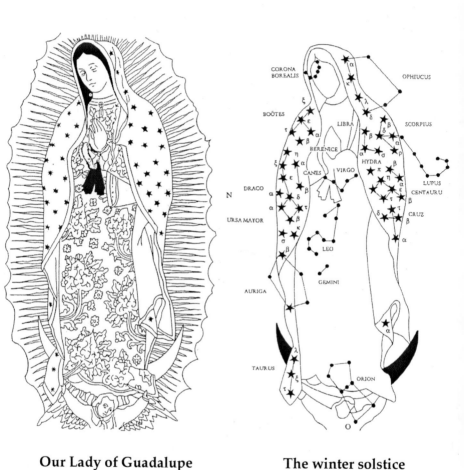

Our Lady of Guadalupe

The winter solstice
on December 12, 1531

**Fig. 4**

# THE END OF THIS ERA

# Chapter 10

## THE WARNINGS OF FATIMA AND AKITA

*Fire will fall from the sky and*
*destroy a great part of humanity.*

Following the experiences of Juan Diego and the bishop, it became a tale of the greatest mass conversion from Aztec paganism to Christianity in the history of the New World and today out of 103 million Mexicans, 90 percent are Catholic and most have portraits of Our Lady of Guadalupe in their homes. And so, let us not talk about the "alleged" apparitions and that "tradition" says this or that. Science has proven indisputably and in numerous ways that the tilma is miraculous and that "a lady" did appear to Juan Diego in 1531.

Over 300 years later, the France of 1870-71 was a country that bothered little about matters of the spirit and the churches were empty. However, Pontmain, a village of about 500 people, was a fortunate exception to the rule of religious indifference. Pontmain's people were farmers and devout believers. When the Franco-Prussian War began in July 1870, thirty-eight young men from Pontmain had been conscripted and were serving in the defence of their homeland. Their families and friends were desperate with fear and concern for them and for the nation.

On January 17, 1871, the Prussians (Germans) were closing in on Laval, the capital of the region in which little Pontmain was situated. About 6 o'clock in the evening and about twenty feet above the rooftops, two children saw a lady. She wore a blue dress once more studded with golden stars. On her head was a crown. Soon after, the stars on her gown seemed to multiply so fast that she appeared to be clothed in gold rather than navy blue (see Fig. 5). The vision slowly vanished at about 9 o'clock in the evening after requesting the people of Pontmain to pray. On the day after

**Fig. 5**
**Our Lady of Hope, Pontmain**

the vision, the relentless advance of the Prussian troops, which had reached the gates of Laval, suddenly stopped and withdrew without fighting. Ten days later on January 28, the armistice was signed and the war was over. The thirty-eight soldiers from Pontmain returned home unscathed. After an extensive enquiry by the Church hierarchy, on February 2, 1872, the "apparition" was officially deemed to be authentic. In fact, the Franco-Prussian War was the one which led to World War I of 1914-1918.

Now, this same "lady," who identified herself as the "Mother of the *true* God" in Guadalupe appeared centuries later on May 13, 1917 during World War I in a village in Portugal called Fatima (named after the daughter of the Prophet Muhammad) to three little children, and said: "I come from heaven. I want you to come here on the 13th of each month until October when I will tell you who I am and what I want." Then on July 13, she said to the children: "The war is going to end soon but if people will not stop offending God, another and more terrible war will begin during the reign of Pius XI. When you see a night illuminated by an unknown light, know that it is the great sign from God that He is going to punish the world by means of war, famine and persecution of the Church...".

Significantly, there was a golden star on the hem of her white gown. The explanation for this is to be found in the Book of Esther. It tells the story of the great and courageous Jewish Queen, one of the wives of King Ahasuerus of Persia (now Iran), who was unaware of Esther's Jewish ethnicity. The Jews were in that land in exile from their homeland Israel after the Babylonians' victory over them. However, the treacherous anti-semitic Haman, who was a high official in king's administration, akin to Prime Minister, had persuaded the king to annihilate them and a date was chosen by lot for their destruction. It was to be on the 13th day of the month it was then that her uncle the noble Mordecai, himself covertly Jewish, entreated Queen Esther to intervene for the Jews. "I shall go to the king in spite of the law, and if I perish, I perish," she immediately said.

In those days no one could approach the king without his prior invitation. Moreover, had the king known that she was Jewish he would ordinarily have expelled her. However, he was so impressed by Esther's courage and beauty that he acceded to her plea and through her intercession, her people were saved from mass annihilation on the designated 13th day of the month. The "Lady from heaven" appeared to the children on the 13th day of each month until October, 1917. In short, she came to Fatima as the "Esther of the New Testament." Her name was indicated on the hem of her gown. The word Esther means "star." Her mission as the Mother of *all* Nations was to try to save the children of the world from annihilation.

It was on October 13 of that year that she performed the historically well-known and authenticated "miracle of the Sun" (our nearest star), which appeared to move from its celestial position and, to the dismay of 70,000 people, was seen to fall towards Earth. They thought that it was the end of their lives and the world. Then after a while, to their relief, at the command of "the lady from heaven" (as seen by the three young visionaries), the Sun retreated to its celestial abode. But prior to that, the three children saw a tableau of the Holy Family with St. Joseph holding the Child Jesus in one arm. He then raised the other arm three times to bless the crowd with the sign of the Cross. Our Lord then appeared in His glorified manhood and blessed the world as St. Joseph had done. Finally, Lucia saw the Blessed Virgin Mary wearing the brown robe of *Our Lady of Mt. Carmel*, holding the brown scapular in her hand and the Child Jesus on her knee. I attach great significance to the appearance of the Child Jesus before Our Lord appeared in His manhood. Let us not forget that redemption began with the Child Jesus!

Now, at that time in 1917, scientists knew very little about nuclear fission and fusion. We now know that in the core of the

Sun there is a nuclear furnace of about 15 million degrees C. (It takes that level of temperature to convert hydrogen into helium by the fusion process). In short, the Sun, like all other stars, is a huge hydrogen bomb that has been exploding continuously for the past five billion years. The apocalyptic message and warning of that event on October 13 is now clear. It was also on that day that she said: "*I am the Lady of the Rosary*" (a weapon in spiritual warfare more powerful than the hydrogen bomb).

Twenty one years later, on the night of January 25, 1938, one of the privileged visionaries (Sr. Lucia) stood at her convent window in Tuy, Portugal, and saw an ominous red glow that lit the entire sky. Looking at the great lights she knew that it was the great sign foretold by "the lady from heaven" on July 13, 1917, that the punishment of the world was at hand. *Notably, at that time Venus and the Sun were forming a conjunction with Jupiter, and Mars was forming a conjunction with Saturn.* In short, in some cases the alignment of planets may be significant.

This light was seen throughout Europe and certain parts of Africa and Asia. It was an Aurora Borealis and it covered an area of 500,000 square kilometers. The rays reached an altitude of 700 km and were accompanied by a strange noise "similar to the sound of burning grass or bush." Millions of people saw it and feared the world was on fire and was about to end. It is named after the Roman goddess of dawn, Aurora, and the Greek name for north wind, Boreas. It appears as a greenish glow or sometimes a faint red as if the sun was rising from an unusual direction. It is also called "the Northern Lights" as it is only visible in the north sky from the northern hemisphere. The corresponding phenomenon in the southern hemisphere is referred to as the Aurora Australis or "the Southern Lights." Typically, the aurora appears either as a diffuse glow or as "curtains" extending in the east-west direction. It is caused by the interaction between the solar wind, Earth's magnetic field and the upper atmosphere (see Figs. 6, 7).

As prophesied, 45 days later World War II started during the reign of Pius XI with the invasion of Austria by Adolph Hitler in March 1938, striking the match that was to set the world on fire. It proved to be the bloodiest conflict ever in known history. Fifty million people, including 6 million European Jews, would die before Berlin fell to the Soviet Red Army on May 8, 1945. Then in

Fig. 6 An Aurora Borealis

Fig. 7 The curtain effect of an Aurora Borealis

August of that year, the United States dropped two atomic bombs on Hiroshima and Nagasaki in Japan, ending the war in the Far East and changing the world. It was the birth of the apocalyptic nuclear age. World War II ended on August 15, 1945. It was the feast of the Assumption of the Blessed Virgin Mary!

Twenty-eight years later in 1973, "the lady from heaven" appeared in Akita, Japan and spoke to Sr. Agnes Sasagawa, a humble nun of the Order of the Handmaids of the Eucharist, in the convent. She spoke through the medium of a statue, which was a replica of the image of *The Lady of all Nations*, as she appeared on March 25, 1945 to the visionary Ida Peerdeman in Amsterdam towards the end of World War II (see Figs. 8, 9).

It was Saturday, 13 October 1973, significantly, the anniversary day and month of the great miracle of the Sun in Fatima. Sr. Agnes related the event: "Taking up my Rosary, I knelt down and

**Fig. 8 Our Lady of all Nations**

**Fig. 9 Our Lady of Fatima and Our Lady of Akita**

made the sign of the Cross. Hardly had I finished when a voice of indescribable beauty came from the statue: 'My dear daughter, listen to what I have to say to you. As I told you, if men do not repent and better themselves, the Father will inflict a terrible punishment on all humanity. It will be a punishment greater than the Flood, such as one will never have seen before. **Fire will fall from the sky** and wipe out a great part of humanity, the good as well as the bad, sparing neither priests nor faithful. The survivors will find themselves so desolate that they will envy the dead. The only arms which will remain for you will be the Rosary and the Sign left by my Son. Each day recite the prayers of the Rosary. With the Rosary, pray for the Pope, the bishops and the priests.

'The work of the devil will infiltrate even into the Church in such a way that one will see cardinals opposing cardinals, bishops against other bishops. The priests who venerate me will be scorned and opposed by their confrères..., churches and altars sacked; the

Church will be filled with those who accept compromise and the demon will press many priests and consecrated souls to leave the service of the Lord. The demon will be especially implacable against souls consecrated to God. The thought of the loss of so many souls is the cause of my sadness. If sins increase in number and gravity, there will no longer be pardon for them…" Later on, she added: "I alone will be able to save you from the calamities which approach. Those who place their confidence in me will be saved.'"

This is a Church-approved apparition but it is disturbing how many of the lay faithful and, above all, how many of the clergy and bishops are unaware of so many approved apparitions of Our lady and Our Lord and their messages. Worse yet, many priests and bishops may know about them yet pay little heed to the messages nor do they teach their congregation about them. *Sola Scriptura* is their motto. It is as if all that Jesus said during his sojourn amongst us on Earth were recorded in the Bible, conveniently forgetting that St. John ended his witness with these words: *"There were many other things that Jesus did, if all were written down, the world itself, I suppose, would not hold all the books that would have to be written"* (John 21:25). And so, God speaks to us first and foremost through the Holy Scriptures, then through the teachings of the Church and also through private revelations.

Now, broadly speaking, "a fire" falling from the sky could be a massive meteor—sometimes called a "fireball," a comet, or a man-made nuclear exchange. That Mary chose the date of October 13 for this apocalyptic message was not by chance and should be linked with the significance of the message behind the miracle of the Sun on October 13, 1917 in Fatima. However, in my opinion, I feel that if there is to be a cataclysm greater than the Flood, such a "punishment" will only come from the hand of God. There may be a limited nuclear exchange, say, between two nations (albeit very unlikely), but not a World War III. Remember also that it is said that on July 12, 1982, Our Lady said in Medjugorje: "The third world war will not take place."

Now, over the years the statue wept 101 times. The weepings of the wooden statue of *Our Lady of Akita* began at about 9 o'clock on the morning of January 4, 1975. It was the first Friday of the month. They stopped on September 15, 1981, the feast of Our Lady of Sorrows!

# Chapter 11

## DEGENERATION, DISASTER, AND WAR

*Let the Holy Spirit live in the hearts of*
*all nations that they may be preserved*
*from degeneration, disaster, and war.*
The Lady of all Nations

Following the end of World War II, a new threat began to take shape. Soviet aggrandizement and Western resistance triggered the Cold War. The Russians were bent on installing friendly regimes in the Eastern European states, which they had liberated and an Iron Curtain descended, as Winston Churchill called it. Indeed, it was inevitable that the Cold War would turn hot. First in Korea, then in Vietnam, communist regimes in the North launched wars to capture by force the non-Communist South countries.

Over the decades other wars and unrests erupted all over the world. In Algeria and other parts of Africa, colonialism was ended by wars of national liberation or by guerrilla movements but those consequences were no less deadly. War erupted in Rwanda, Congo, Algeria, Angola, Uganda, Chad, Namibia, Burundi, Eritrea, Ethiopia, Sierra Leone, and other countries. In fact, every nation in sub-Saharan Africa has either been devastated by war or borders a nation that has been. There were also ethnic or religious wars in Israel, Sudan, India, Kashmir, Indonesia, Malaysia, Afghanistan, Sri Lanka, the Philippines, Northern Ireland, Nigeria, Liberia and in Yugoslavia. There were also conflicts in the Central and South American continents, including Nicaragua, Argentina, Chile, Colombia, Peru, Cuba and San Salvador. The world is at war.

Furthermore, children who grew up surrounded by war now perceived it as a normal way of life and in several parts of the world children are abducted and recruited into the armed forces. According to a recent report by the United Nations Children's Emergency

Fund (UNICEF), millions of children throughout the world are also being bought and sold like chattels and used as sex slaves. The report estimates that as many as 400,000 children and women are subjected to commercial sexual exploitation in India, between 244,000 and 325,000 in the United States, 200,000 in Thailand and 175,000 in Eastern and Central Europe. It also estimates that 100,000 women and children are also sexually exploited in the Philippines, Taiwan and Brazil, and 35,000 in West Africa.

The societal degeneration does not stop there. Columbia, Peru and Bolivia remain the primary sources of the coca leaf and cocaine trafficking and abuse, once seen as concerns particularly for the United States, are increasingly becoming global in nature, not to mention the large-scale opium fields of Afghanistan. This trafficking involves billions of dollars every year and has led to great increases in kidnapping, violence and murders. Organized criminal groups also use these profits to obtain power and to finance other criminal groups, terrorists and insurgencies. According to the *World Drug Report 2004*, published by the United Nations Office on Drugs and Crime, some 13 million people around the world are also affected by cocaine. This is the degenerate world in which we live. In addition, the 20th century and beyond, following an egoistic and hedonistic sexual revolution, also reached levels of permissiveness, prostitution, promiscuity and pornography, openly displayed vulgarity, and corruption in politics and business, which seem to have few parallels in known history.

Internet pornography has now become a billion dollar industry and statistics have recorded that every second 28,258 internet users are viewing porn sites and every 30 minutes a pornographic video is being created in the United States with a revenue exceeding the combined revenues of ABC, CBS and NBC. The top video porn producers worldwide are the United States, Brazil, The Netherlands, Spain, Japan and Russia. Meanwhile more than a billion people in the world live below the poverty line. In fact, more than half of the planet is one huge slum. We have not been good caretakers of the Landlord's creation.

But even more disturbing, a nuclear World War III has been a constant threat to mankind over the years. Paul R. Ehrlich of the Department of Biological Sciences at Stanford University put a large scale thermal nuclear war in its perspective. He estimated that the blasts alone would be expected to cause 750 million deaths. Dr. Paul J. Crutzen, Director of the Atmospheric Chemistry Division of the Max Planck Institute for Chemistry in Mainz, Federal Republic of Germany, predicted that there would be a production of between 300 and 400 million tons of smoke, 30 percent of which would be strongly light-absorbing elemental carbon. This atmosphere of soot and dust from the northern hemisphere would soon be transported to the southern hemisphere. Food shortages resulting from the inevitable collapse of the agricultural system, the shut down of food transportation and distribution systems, and the incapability of crop plants to survive the climatic changes, could also cause hundreds of millions or billions of humans worldwide to starve to death.

Dr. Carl Sagan, Professor of Astronomy and Space Sciences and the Director of the Laboratory for Planetary Studies at Cornell University, talking in 1983 about the possibility of a nuclear exchange, also said: "It is certainly true that we have gone thirty-eight years without a nuclear war. Who knows, we might be able to survive for some longer period of time. But would you want to bet your life on it? I do not guarantee that this is a perfect analogy, but the situation reminds me of a man falling from the top of a high building, saying to an office worker through an open window as he passes by, 'So far, so good.'"

But it is the religious wars which are now threatening world peace as never before through divisions and the emergence of so-called militant Islamic fundamentalism with its suicide bombers and their total disregard for the sanctity of *life,* killing themselves and others *in the name of God*! Indeed, religious wars are superseding ethnic, civil, and other wars in severity and in their potential for a total global disaster and conflagration. Of special concern today is the Middle East Israeli/Palestinian crisis, the nuclear ambitions of North Korea and especially Iran, with its threat that Israel should be wiped off the map. This could certainly be a spark to ignite a nuclear war.

Also of very great concern are the dramatic increases in natural disasters over the years which are occurring all over the world claiming lives and affecting economies (see Graph 1). It is said that the suddenness with which the earthquake in Kobe, Japan, struck on Tuesday, 17 January 1995 was awesome. The tremor lasted only

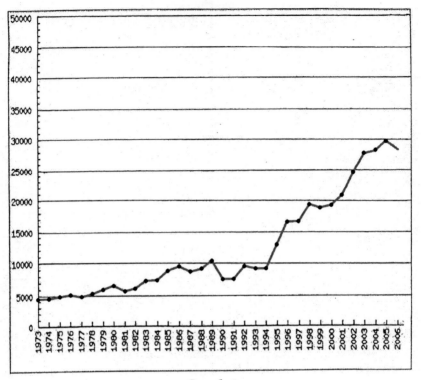

**Graph 1**
**The number of earthquakes has increased over recent years**

20 seconds, registering 7.2 on the Richter scale, but in that short time, 6,433 people died, nearly 27,000 were injured, more than 45,000 homes were destroyed and over 300,000 became homeless. According to witnesses, possibly the most frightening part was the sound. This was not the dull rumble of thunder. This was a deafening, *roaring* sound coming from everywhere and nowhere, and it sounded like the end of the world.

Nine years later, the Indian Ocean earthquake was an underseas quake that occurred on December 26, 2004. It triggered a series of devastating tsunamis, killing more than 225,000 people in eleven countries and inundating coastal communities with waves up to 100 feet high. With a magnitude of 9.1 and 9.3, it is the second largest earthquake ever recorded on a seismograph. It had the longest duration observed (between 8.4 and 10 minutes) and the energy released by it was equivalent to 9,560 gigatons of TNT, equivalent to

550 million times that of the atomic bomb which fell on Hiroshima in 1945. This massive release of energy altered the Earth's rotation very slightly and caused the planet to wobble and tilt 1 inch on its axis. Add to all these catastrophes the ever increasing tornadoes and hurricanes, like Katrina and Ike, destroying cities to rubble and causing many deaths.

But a major cataclysm with consequences much worse and with greater releases of energy could be caused by an impact or impacts with massive asteroids. It needs to be appreciated that each day about a million meteors, captives of gravity, pass into Earth's atmosphere. The vast majority of them are smallish objects that heat up and disintegrate as they enter the planet's invisible barrier of air, but a few of them are of such magnitude as to change the course of history. Those who have researched the messages of *Our Lady of all Nations*, which were given to Ida Peerdeman in Amsterdam, will recall that on August 15, 1950 and again on March 20, 1963, she said to Ida: *"There are meteors. Watch out for them. There will be calamities; there will be cataclysms."* And so, it seems that the warning in Akita that "fire will fall from the sky" may refer to a large meteor which will leave its orbit in the asteroid belt and come between the Sun and Earth. Recall also that meteors are called "fireballs."

The dinosaurs were once lords of the Earth, the largest creatures and the most powerful. There is now general acceptance that their reign came to a sudden and catastrophic end approximately 65 million years ago at a time of the collision of planet Earth with a large asteroid that fell in the general vicinity of what is now the Yucatan peninsula (later to become the homeland of the Mayans!). But how can such an impact kill hundred-ton dinosaurs and other creatures as well as plant life halfway around the world? The answer lies in the probability that for months or even years afterwards, the Earth would have been darkened and then cooled, a sort of nuclear winter, which could not sustain life. The plight of the dinosaurs stumbling across the frozen and devastated landscape, unable to find either food or warmth, can only be imagined.

And so, it has happened before and sooner or later a large comet or meteor will indeed strike Earth, the consequences of which you can be sure would be catastrophic. If such a strike occurred in mid-ocean, multiple tsunamis in the 100-foot range would cause worldwide damage, especially to coastline areas. If the strike occurred on land, the blast would cause tons upon tons of ash and rock to be thrown into the stratosphere where it would act to reduce the solar radiation and threaten the planet with darkness and perhaps some sort of ice age. Indeed, the blend of mischief that asteroids and comets bring—floods darkness, fire, rending asunder—is well-known. As Carl Sagan wrote: "If a comet of a few kilometers in diameter hits Earth, the sky will become so hot from the impact that wildfires would be ignited all over the world, the sky worldwide would be on fire and moreover there would be pitch darkness." Comets are indeed celestial missiles.

Sagan also cautioned that "none of the near earth objects are known to have orbits that would impact the Earth in the next few centuries but tomorrow one might be discovered that will. There might be a comet with our name on it. In short, a cosmic doomsday clock may be ticking away even now. There is also the remote possibility of a long-period comet soaring out of the Kuiper belt on a beeline for planet Earth with only a few months' notice to us." And so, while it is believed that comets brought water and life to Earth, they can also destroy worlds.

On 7 April 2004, Dr. Michael D. Griffin, Administrator National Aeronautics and Space Administration (NASA), in a testimony to the United States Senate Subcommittee on Science, Technology and Space Hearing on Near Earth Objects, said: "Thank you for giving me this opportunity to comment on the greatest natural threat to the long-term survivability of mankind, an asteroid impact with Earth. The effects of an impact are so catastrophic that it is essential to prepare a defense against such an occurrence... Impacts with diameters greater than 1 km could result in worldwide damage and the possible elimination of the human race...".

Then on 7 May 2008, Dr. George T. Whitesides, Executive Director, of the National Space Society, speaking before a US Subcommittee on Space, Aeronautics, and Related Science, warned: "There are vast numbers of asteroids in near-earth orbits... If we do nothing, sooner or later we will be hit by an asteroid large enough to threaten life on Earth... In 1908 a small asteroid (perhaps 50 meters across) hit Tunguska, Siberia and flattened 60 million trees... That asteroid was so small, it never even hit the ground, just exploded in mid-air. If it had arrived 4 hours and 52 minutes later, it is calculated that it would have hit St. Petersburg, which at that time was the capital of Russia with a population of a few hundred thousand. The city would have ceased to exist."

Apropos this, NASA astronaut Ed Liu told US scientists in April 2004 that (hopefully) an asteroid deflection mission could be ready for flight by 2015. US Congress then ordered NASA to determine the alternatives that it would employ to divert an asteroid if one were found to be on collision course with our planet. *And so, governments are quite aware of this possible threat.*

# THE END OF THIS ERA

# Chapter 12

## BIBLICAL PROPHECY
## AND
## THE END OF THIS ERA

*When the Lord saw how great was man's wickedness on earth, and how no desire that his heart conceived was ever anything but evil, he regretted that he had made man on the earth, and his heart was grieved. So the Lord said: "I will wipe out from the earth the men whom I have created."*

(Genesis 6:5-7)

Speaking about the great Flood, Graham Hancock quoted the Book of Enoch where it is recorded that "Noah saw that the earth had tilted and that its destruction was near, and cried out in a bitter voice: 'Tell me what is being done on the earth that the earth is so afflicted and shaken...'" While this book does not form part of the Canon of Scripture for most of the Christian Churches, the Ethiopian Orthodox Church still regards it to be inspired Scripture.

"Noah saw that the earth had tilted." This fascinated me. The Indian Ocean earthquake of December 2004 with its tsunamis caused planet Earth to tilt 1 inch on its axis, but following a much greater cataclysm, there could be a massive upheaval on Earth with an attendant shift in land masses and a *significant* tilt in the axis of the planet. This could result in the survivors seeing a different constellation of stars in the sky from any one point. For them it will be *a new heaven and a new earth*.

Strangely enough, the gifted Mayans with their unsurpassed mathematical and astronomical knowledge actually knew about the Flood. (There is debate as to whether the Flood was restricted to the Mesopotamia area or the whole world). They believed that it was the end of one of several cataclysms which planet Earth had experienced over the many millennia. They prophesied that the next cataclysm will be at the end of the "fifth sun," which is calculated to occur on *December 21, 2012*. Interestingly, the traditional narratives of the Hopi Indians give a somewhat similar history and prophecy. They live in Northeast Arizona and may have arrived in their current location 5,000-10,000 years ago. Their ancestors, the Anasazi, appeared to have been related to the Aztecs.

Traditionally, the Hopi are a religious people. The name Hopi is believed by some to be derived from "Hopita," meaning those who are "peaceful ones." To be Hopi is to strive toward this concept, which involves a state of total reverence and respect for all things, to be at peace with these things and to live in accordance with the Creator. They too believe that we are walking in darkness with a virtual sword of Damocles hanging over us, but notably, the Hopi elders, the Mayans and the Aztecs do not prophesy that it will be the end of the world. They believe that following this era, the next will be one from cataclysm to enlightenment and from world war to world peace and spiritual awakening.

As Hancock wrote: "My research has convinced me that there was an advanced civilization long, long, ago that was destroyed in a terrible cataclysm. I fear that our own civilization may be destroyed by a similar cataclysm. When human beings from around the globe, and from many different cultures, share a powerful and overwhelming intuition that a cataclysm is approaching, we are within our rights to ignore them. And when the voices of our distant ancestors, descended to us through myths and sacred architecture, speak to us of the physical obliteration of a great civilization in remote antiquity (and tell us that our own civilization is in jeopardy), we are entitled, if we wish, to block our ears... However, it would be foolish to disregard what they seem to be saying. And what they seem to be saying to us is that cyclical, recurrent and near-total destructions of mankind are part and parcel of life on this planet, that such destructions have occurred many times before and that they will certainly occur again. Scholars normally attribute these myths to the fantasies of ancient poets. But what if the scholars are wrong?"

I am one of those who, like Graham Hancock, respects the prophecies given by the Mayans, the Aztecs and the Hopi Indians. Indeed, it will be foolish of anyone to disregard them *completely* as just myths. It would, however, also be foolhardy of me to accept that, in spite of their great mathematical and astronomical genius and heavenly gifts, any of the ancients can predict the day, the hour and the exact year of the next "sun." As it is written in Mark 13:32: *"but as for the day or hour, nobody knows it, neither the angels in heaven, nor the Son; no one but the Father."* In fact, I could find no record that they had ever correctly predicted the exact date of the end of the previous "suns" or eras.

It is well-known that this present civilization has become increasingly degenerate. This degeneration also includes the numerous men of the cloth, who have abused young boys and women. It includes the recent abomination of same sex marriages, an abomination not previously recorded in known history (not even in the days of Sodom and Gomorrah), an abomination which also aims to destroy the family unit as designed by God, an abomination which has been sanctioned by the Episcopal Anglican Church in America with one of its bishops marrying his male consort of 20 years in a civil ceremony followed by a religious service of thanksgiving in a church. And the world Anglican communion is still debating what should be its stand!

The world, especially the United States, is now also in the throes of a major economic recession and collapse, which could probably be worse than the Great Depression of 1929. But didn't *Our Lady of all Nations* also warn us about this in her apparitions in Amsterdam?: "Great powers will crumble and political and economic conflicts will break out" (March 28, 1945), and "There are economic and natural disasters that will strike the world" (November 15, 1951).

But much more serious in the eyes of heaven is the spiritual recession in today's world to the extent that, for example, the Spain of Queen Isabel the Catholic, which evangelized Catholicism throughout the New World, was one of the first countries to sanction same sex marriage as have some states in the United States of America, a country whose Pledge of Allegiance includes the words "One nation under God." But prayer is now not allowed in the nation's schools!

This world is also steeped in fear, violence, brutality, wars, lust, confusion, calumny, slander, and greed. Indeed, many mystics have warned that the sin of the world today is worse than at the time of Noah and it is prophesied in the Bible that there will be a major cataclysm like the one in Noah's time, except that it will be the fire next time: *"By water that world was then destroyed; it was overwhelmed by the deluge. The present heavens and earth are reserved by God's word for fire; they are kept for the day of judgment, the day when godless men would be destroyed"* (2 Peter 3:7).

2 Peter 2 also talks about the sin and degeneration of this world: *"These men pour abuse on things of which they are ignorant. They act like creatures of instinct, brute animals born to be caught and destroyed. Because of their decadence they too will be destroyed, suffering the reward of their wickedness. Thinking daytime revelry a delight, they are stain and defilement as they share your feasts in a spirit of seduction. Constantly on the lookout for a woman, theirs is again a never-ending quest for sin. They lure the weaker types. Their hearts are trained in greed... An accursed lot they are. ...Note this first of all: in the last days mocking, sneering men who are ruled by their passions would arrive on scene...".*

And in Mark 13:8-25: *"Nation will rise against nation, one kingdom against another. There would be famine and pestilence and earthquakes in many places... If a man is on the roof terrace, he must not come down or enter his house to get anything out of it...Those times will be more distressful than any between God's work of creation and now, and for all time to come. Indeed, had the Lord not shortened the period, not a person would be saved. But for the sake of those he has chosen, he has shortened the days. Immediately after the stress of that period, the sun will be darkened, the moon will not shed her light, stars will fall from the sky, and the hosts of heaven will be shaken loose."*

My humble interpretation of the latter two lines is that they may refer to the large quantities of dust and smoke as a result of a major cataclysm from a huge meteor or comet, which will cause the Sun and Moon to be darkened for days and that the "stars falling from the sky" may refer to numerous meteor showers ("falling stars") as described in Chapter 1, and which frequently accompany comets and meteors. They have been seen before (Fig. 10).

Interestingly, as late as 1835, a lecturer at The Royal Institute in London concluded that the orbital inclination and eccentricities of comets do "not depend upon physical laws but upon the will of the Creator." As Carl Sagan once said: "Certainly, it does seem strange that a purely haphazard event could possibly destroy the Earth." In concert with this, in 1850 Thomas Dick (1774-1857), known for his work on astronomy and philosophy, combining science and

**Fig. 10 An eyewitness rendition of the great
Leonid Meteor Shower of November 13, 1833**

Christianity, once wrote: "Believing that every object and every event in the universe is arranged and directed by an omnipotent Contriver, we must admit that when the Almighty formed the wondrous plan of creation, foreseeing the end and the beginning, he arranged the periods and the velocities of comets in such a manner that, although occasionally crossing the planetary orbits, they should not pass these orbits at a time when the planets were in their immediate vicinity. And should such an event ever occur, we may rest assured that it is in perfect accordance with the plan and the will of the Creator, and that it is on the whole subservient to the happiness and order of the intelligent universe, and intended by the Divine government." This is an interesting "theology." In fact,

Edmund Halley after whom the famous comet was named once proposed that the biblical Flood was produced by a comet!

Twenty-eight years after the end of World War I in 1917, World War II ended in 1945 with the surrender of Japan after the dropping of atomic bombs on Hiroshima and Nagasaki, and 28 years later in 1973, Our Lady chose to appear in Akita, Japan, the only country which had experienced the annihilating effects of nuclear energy. She warned the world about a fire falling from the sky. Following this Akita warning, once more, another 28 years later on September 11, 2001 (9/11), "a fire" did fall from the sky from two planes, which crashed into the twin towers of the World Trade Center in New York City. It was a mini-cataclysm, birth pangs, shall we say, and a prelude of things to come on a much larger scale. It was the official beginning of a new type of war in the 21st century—international terrorism. It was the fulfillment of the prophecy which the *Lady of all Nations* made in Amsterdam on August 29, 1945 after the end of World War II when she referred to "a new, yet strange war in the distant future, which will cause terrible havoc."

The recurrent intervals of 28 years excited my curiosity. A sidereal lunar month is a period of approximately 28 days. It is the length of time taken by the Moon in its orbit around the Earth to return to the same point as viewed against the background of the stars. Could the 28-day intervals be therefore related to a Marian symbol in that in Mariology, Mary is likened to the Moon and her Son to the Sun, or is it just coincidence?

Significantly, "the lady from heaven" has frequently associated herself with a celestial body or phenomenon. These were seen, for example, in Guadalupe in 1531 when she was standing on the crescent Moon and adorned with a constellation of stars on her gown; in 1871 in Pontmain with numerous moving stars on her dress; in 1917 in Fatima with the miracle of the Sun; in 1938 with an Aurora Borealis; and in 1981 in Medjugorje, where she appeared wearing a crown of twelve stars (Rev.12:1).

And so, I suspect that in similar vein a celestial warning will be given by her close to the date when the "fire" (of whatever nature) will fall from the sky. However, it is also possible that this warning "sign" may well be a different, rare and startling celestial phenomenon, which will have to be seen this time *throughout the world* and not as the "Northern Lights" of 1938 which was only seen in Europe and North Africa in keeping with the battlefields of World War II. One possible example could be the re-appearance of "two suns" as was seen in 203 BC (see Chapter 1) or something as rare as that and which will be seen by the whole world.

I mention this because of a recent prophecy given by Our Lady to a visionary whom the renowned and experienced Mariologist Fr. René Laurentin of France has thoroughly investigated (including scientific tests performed by leading French and American scientists, proving that she is truly in ecstasy during the apparitions. It is totally impossible to fake ecstasy). He, like numerous other priests, theologians, scientists and countless of the lay faithful, including myself, through our intimate contact and knowledge of her, have absolutely no doubt about her authenticity. However, because of the well-known tradition of tardiness by Church authorities in approving or reversing disapprovals of authentic apparitions (e.g., St. Padre Pio and St. Faustina Kowalska, whose diary of her visions were placed in the *Index of Forbidden Books* for over 20 years) and because I do believe that time is now relatively short, I will record a small part of the message of Our Lady given to her on June 1, 2008: "When you see two suns appearing on the horizon, you must know that this is a time of change, a time of this new beginning about which I have spoken to you before. After you see the two suns, there is only a short time before you will see a tremendous change in weather. After this, there are more changes to come… After a while, you will see a time when there is another body in orbit around your solar system coming between the Earth and the Sun and leading to tremendous devastation…"

To verify whether this solar phenomenon had any precedence, in a recent telephone conversation with Mike Brown, the co-discoverer of the 10th planet Eris, and who has been listed among the hundred most influential people by *Time* magazine, he gave me his opinion of how "two suns" may truly be seen *on the horizon* and suggested that it could be due to a supernova in our galaxy. A typical supernova is an explosive event of tremendous energy output generated by the gravitational collapse of a massive star (one many times larger than our Sun). He recalled that in 203 BC, "two suns" were seen in the sky. There were intervals of daylight during the night. Another appearance of "two suns" was in 185 AD. Astronomers recorded the appearance of a bright star like a Sun in the sky and observed that it took about eight months to fade from the sky. Yet another one was observed on July 4, 1054 AD. It remained visible in daylight for 23 days and was visible in the night sky for 653 days. It eventually faded from view on April 17,1056 AD. This explosion appeared in the constellation of Taurus. As to seeing it *"on the horizon,"* this is because it would be difficult to see the supernova in conjunction with the Sun while the bright Sun was high in the sky and it is usually only possible to see it when the Sun is very low *on the horizon* in the evening or at dawn when there would seem to be "two suns," one possibly larger than the other (Fig. 11).

Now, it is reported that in 1982 Our Lady said in Medjugorje,

**Fig. 11 Two Suns on the Horizon**

an apparition site as yet to be fully approved by the Church: "These apparitions are the last in the world." If so, it is my personal belief that just as she first appeared in Medjugorje holding the Child Jesus in her arm, so will she appear with the Child in her last apparition in this era *wherever that may be.* It will be Mary as the *Theotokos* as she is always depicted in the Eastern Church.

I do accept that we are deserved of a "punishment" from God, the Father of Mankind, and that we are in the last days of this era (not the end of the world). In fact, hasn't God been very patient with us considering the progressive and escalating degeneration in the world? But what will it take to change the behaviour of mankind other than a punishment? Indeed, the Blessed Virgin has said on many occasions that she, as a loving mother, has been holding back the hand of Justice of her Son for years, however I believe that we are now close to the end of the ever so long period of His Mercy since only very few have responded to her call. That is why she is crying all over the world. However, I feel that because of the special and holy grounds on Earth trodden by Our Lord and the places where He chose to send His mother to appear in the world, these places will be protected from the cataclysmic punishment. In addition, how else could the Gospel be preserved for the next era of peace! These will be the safe havens and sanctuaries.

So said, my Marian research over the past 25 years leads me to believe that among the many havens will be certain parts of Israel, Guadalupe in Mexico, La Salette, the Rue du Bac, Lourdes and Pontmain in France, Banneux and Beauraing in Belgium, an area in Amsterdam in Holland, Medjugorje in Croatia, Betania in Venezuela, and parts of Maryland in the United States, especially Emmitsburg and its environs. In this respect, it is interesting that almost all of the shrines where the "Mother of the *true* God" has appeared have been on mounts much higher than sea level! It could well be that this will be the "Age of Mary" as Fr. F.W. Faber wrote in his Preface to St. Louis De Montfort's classic Marian work *True Devotion to Mary.*

Now, Noah and his family were the only ones saved in the ark which God had instructed him to build: *"This is how you shall build it. The length of the ark shall be three hundred cubits, its width fifty cubits, and its height thirty cubits… Put an entrance at the side of the ark, which you shall make with bottom, second and third decks"* (Genesis 6:15-16). This three-storey ark has been likened to Mary and her link with the Holy Trinity. She is the mother of the Son, but she is also the daughter of the Father and the bride of the Holy Spirit. As such she has become for Christians a locus of encounter with the three Divine Persons, and as Noah received his children into the ark and they were saved, so, too, will all those who seek shelter in the living ark, Mary.

But she is also the Ark of the Covenant, or more precisely, the living Ark of the Mediator of the New Covenant. The ancient Ark of the Covenant contained the two tablets of the Law, but at Mary's conception of Jesus this living Ark immediately contained within her womb, not the tablets of the Law but the Lawgiver Himself, and just also as the ancient Ark of the Covenant contained a ciborium with some of the miraculous manna which fell from heaven to feed the Israelites, Mary contained in her womb, not the miraculous manna, which fed them on their journey to the Promised Land and yet they died, but the true Bread of Life, which gives us everlasting life.

Interestingly, in my research for my first book *Mary Ark of the Covenant*, among many other places, I travelled to Ethiopia and Israel. In the latter country, I visited the site where now stands the Basilica of Mary, Ark of the Covenant. It is built on a hill in Kiriath Jearim just 25 miles outside of Jerusalem where the ancient Ark of the Covenant had remained in the house of Abinadab for about 50 years all through the reign of Samuel and Saul before David took it from the house in 1004 BC (Samuel 6:19-21). There I saw on the steeple of the church, a concrete depiction of the ancient Ark of the Covenant, flanked at the top by two winged cherubs at both ends, and between the wings stood the Blessed Virgin Mary holding the Child Jesus in her left arm. The Child, in turn, was holding up the Eucharist between His right thumb and index finger (see Figs. 12-15). Is this therefore a herald of the much-talked-about Eucharistic reign of the Child Jesus?

**Fig. 12 The Basilica of Mary, the Ark of the Covenant**

Fig. 13 Front View

Fig. 14 Side View

Fig. 15
The Child Jesus
holding the Eucharist

As she said to Juan Diego in the primogenitus Marian shrine of the New World, Guadalupe: "Know for certain my dearest and youngest son, that I am the perfect and perpetual Virgin Mary, Mother of the *true* God, through whom everything lives, the Lord of all things, who is Master of creation and of Heaven and Earth, I ardently desire that a temple be built here for me where I will show and offer all my love, my compassion, my help, and my protection to the people. I am your merciful Mother, Mother of all who live united in this land, and of all mankind, of all those who love me, of those who cry to me, of those who seek me, of those who have confidence in me. Here I will hear their weeping and their sorrow, and will remedy and alleviate their sufferings, their necessities and their misfortunes... Am I not here, I, who am your Mother? Are you not under my shadow and protection? Am I not the cause of your joy? Are you not in the folds of my mantle? In the crossing of my arms? What more do you need?"

Now, her Son once said to the saintly stigmatist of Belgium, Berthe Petit, highly respected by Cardinal Désiré Mercier, the Primate of Belgium, and Cardinal Francis Bourne, Archbishop of Westminster and Primate of England: *"The title of 'Immaculate' belongs to the whole being of My Mother and not specially to her heart. This title flows from my gratuituous gift to the Virgin who was to give me birth. My Mother has acquired for her heart the title of 'Sorrowful' by sharing generously in all the sufferings of My Heart and My Body from the crib to the Cross. There is not one of these sorrows which did not pierce the heart of My Mother. Living image of My crucified Body, her virginal flesh bore the invisible marks of My wounds as her heart felt the sorrows of My own. Nothing could ever tarnish the incorruptibility of her Immaculate Heart.*

*"The title of 'Sorrowful' belongs therefore to the heart of My Mother, and more than any other, this title is dear to her because it springs from the union of her heart with Mine in the redemption of humanity. This title has been acquired by her through her full participation in My Calvary, and it precedes the gratuitous title 'Immaculate' which My love bestowed upon her by a singular privilege...* **Recourse to My Mother under the title and invocation I wish for her universally, 'Sorrowful and Immaculate Heart of Mary, pray for us,' is the last help I shall give before the end of time...** *It is as a Son that I have conceived this devotion for My Mother. It is as God that I impose it."*

But it is also the ultimate message of Fatima. So said, it is important to appreciate that the apparitions of Our Lady to the three children which began in that small village in Portugal ended in the convent in Pontevedra, Spain where Lucia (1907-2005), the eldest of the visionaries, was a postulant. On December 10, 1925, while she was in the convent, Our Lady of Fatima came with the Child Jesus who stood beside her lifted on a luminous cloud. In one hand she held her heart encircled by thorns (Fig. 16). Four years later, on June 13, 1929, Sr. Lucia had her last apparition of Our Lady in the novitiate chapel of St. Dorothy in Tuy, Spain. Suddenly the whole chapel was illuminated by a supernatural light and a Cross of light appeared above the altar reaching to the ceiling. In a bright light at the upper part of the Cross could be seen the face of a man and his body to the waist (*the Father*). On his breast there was a dove also of light (*the Holy Spirit*) and nailed to the Cross was the body of another man (*the Son*). Our Lady was beneath the right arm of the Cross. It was Our Lady of Fatima with her Immaculate Heart within a crown of thorns and flames. It was the **Sorrowful and**

Fig. 16 The Child Jesus and the Mother of Sorrows

**Fig. 17 The Sorrowful and Immaculate Heart of Mary**

**Immaculate Heart** of the Co-Redemptrix (Fig. 17, 18).

As the late Fr. Joseph A. Pellitier once wrote: 'The Co-redemption of Mary is the doctrinal truth expressed by the title the **Sorrowful and Immaculate Heart of Mary** and is what Our Lord wants recognized in the Church in a worldwide basis." As explained in the World Apostolate of Fatima's booklet **Sorrowful and Immaculate Heart of Mary**: "At Fatima Our Blessed Lady asked that her Immaculate Heart, the free gift from God's grace, should be honoured. But it would not have been in accordance with her perfect humility had she exalted her own merits in proclaiming the glory of her Sorrowful Heart. It is therefore incumbent on the faithful, as it were, to complete the message of Fatima by obtaining, through ardent prayer, the consecration of the world to the **Sorrowful and Immaculate Heart** of the Mother of our Saviour."

And so, this is an *urgent* call for individuals, homes and countries to be dedicated and consecrated to Mary under this title. It is the

**Fig. 18 The Sorrowful and Immaculate Heart of Mary
Beneath the Right Arm of the Cross**

refuge and hope of the "banished children of Eve." It is the last
help that her Son will give before the end of time. We must also
remember that she said in Akita: "The only help left for you is the
rosary and the sign (*the Eucharist*) left by my Son." It is the sign of
His great Love.

President Franklin Delano Roosevelt once said during a time of
great distress: "The only thing we have to fear is fear itself." Indeed,
there are many who believe that time is short, very short, but there is
no time now for fear. There is only time for change. And by change
I do not mean a change of government. Only a *spiritual* change
and the consecration to the **Sorrowful and Immaculate Heart of
Mary** can save the world and mitigate the inevitable chastisement
to come.

# REFERENCES

Adams, Fred, *Origins of Existence*, The Free Press, New York, 2002.

Allegre, Claude and Schneider, Stephen, "The Evolution of Earth," *Scientific American*, Volume 15, Number 2, 2005.

Armstrong, Karen, *Holy War, the Crusades And Their Impact On Today's World*, Anchor Books, New York, 1992.

Arnaldo, Carlos, A., *Child Abuse on the Internet*, Bezghahn Books, New York and UNESCO Publishing, Paris, 2001.

Asimon, Isaac, *Guide To Earth And Space*, Fawcett Crest, New York, 1991.

Atal, Yogest and Oyen, Else, *Poverty and Participation in Local Society*, 1997

Baagil, H.M., *Christian Muslim Dialogue*, Islamic Propagation Centre International (UK), Printed for the British 8 Foreign Bible Society, 1930.

Bartholomew, C., *A Scientist Researches Mary Mother of All Nations*, Queenship Publishing Company, California, USA, 1999.

Boslow, John, *Stephen Hawking's Universe*, Avon Books, New York, 1980.

Bousso, Raphael and Polchinski, "Joseph", *Scientific American*, September, 2004.

Brother Francis, *Philosophia Perennis. Volume 111: Cosmology*, Loreto Publications, USA, 2000.

Cairns-Smith, A.G., *Some Clues to the Origin of Life*, Cambridge University Press, 1985.

Cech, T. R., "The Efficiency and Versatility of Catalytic RNA: Implication for an RNA World," *Gene*, 135, 33-36, 1993.

Churchill, Winston, *The Second World War*, Pimlico, London, 2002.

Clarke, Peter, *The World's Religions*. The Reader's Digest Association Limited, London, 1993.

Clark, Ronald W., *Einstein: The Life and Times*, Avon Books, New York, 1984.

Collins, Francis S. , *The Language of God*, Free Press, New York, 2006

Connor, Steve and Kingman, Sharon, *The Search for the Virus*, Penguin Books, 1998.

# REFERENCES

Consolmagno, Br. Guy, *Intelligent Life in the Universe?*, Catholic Truth Society, London, 2005.

Darwin, C., *The Origin of Species*, Penguin Classics, London, 1985.

Davies, Paul, *God And The New Physics*, Penguin Books, London, 1983.

Davies, P., *The Fifth Medical: The Search for the Origin of Life*, Penguin Books, London, 1998.

Davies, Paul, *The Mind Of God*, Simon & Shuster, New York, 1992.

Davis, P., Kenyan, D., Phaxton, C., *Of Pandas And People*, Haughton Publishing Company, Dallas, Texas, 1999.

Dawkins, R., *The Blind Watchmaker*, W.W. Norton, New York, 1986.

de Duve, C., *Blueprint for a Cell: The Nature and Origin of Life*, Neil Patterson Publishers, Burlington, NC, 1991.

Dimbleby, Jonathan, *The Palestinians*, Quarter Books Limited, London, 1979.

Dyson, Freeman, *Origins of Life*, Cambridge University Press, 1999.

Eigen, M., Gardiner, W., Schuster, P and Winckler-Oswatitch, R., "The Origin of Genetic Information," *Scientific American*, 244 (4), 88-118, 1981.

Elias, Jamal J., and Lewis, Nancy D., *Islam*, Alpha, A Peaarson Education Company, 1999.

Elias, Jamel J., *Islam*, Pearson Education Inc., Publishing as Alpha Book 2003.

Fergusson, Niall, *The War of the World*, The Penguin Press, New York, 2006.

Filly, R. A., "Ultrasound Evaluation during the First Trimester." In Callen P. W. (ed), *Ultrasonography in Obstetrics and Gynecology*, W. B. Saunders, Philadelphia, 1994.

Folsmome, C., Life: "Origin and Evolution," *Scientific American*, Special Publication, 1979.

Fortey, Richard, *Life: An Unauthorized Biography*, Flamingo, Harper Collins Publishers, London, 1997.

Garlick, M., *The Expanding Universe*, Dorling Kindersley, London, 2002

Gilbert, W., The RNA World, Nature, 319, 618, 1986.

Grotzinger, J., "Biostratigraphic and Geochronologic Constraints on Early Animal Evolution," *Science*, 270:598-604, 1995.

Hancock, Graham. *Fingerprints of the Gods,* Crown Trade Paperbacks, New York, 1995

Hawking, Stephen, *A Brief History Of Time,* Guild Publishing, London, 1998.

Heeren, Fred, *Show Me God,* Day Star Publications, Inc, Wheeling, Illinois, 1997.

Hoffman, Bruce, *Inside Terrorism,* Columbia University Press, New York, 1998.

Horgan, J., "Trends in Evolution," *Scientific American,* February, 1991.

Horgan, J., "In the Beginning," *Scientific American,* 117, 1991.

Horgan, J., "Profile: Francis H. C. Crick," *Scientific American,* February, 1992.

Horrie, Chris and Chippindale, Peter, *What is Islam?,* Virgin Books, London, 1993.

Jastrow, W., *God And The Astronomers,* W. W. Norston & Company, Inc., New York/London, 1992.

John Paul II, *Crossing The Threshold Of Hope,* Alfred A. Knopf, New York, 1994.

Joyce, G. F., "RNA Evolution and the Origins of Life," *Nature,* 338, 217-224, 1989.

Kerr, R., "Did Darwin Get It All Right?," *Science,* 267:1421, 1995.

Lambert, Lance, *The Uniqueness of Israel,* Kingsway Publishing, Eastbournes, Sussex, 1980.

Laqueur, Walter, *The New Terrorism,* Phoenix Press, London, 2001.

Lewis, Bernard, *Islam and the West,* New York and Oxford: Oxford University Press, 1993.

Lewis, Bernard, *The Middle East: A Brief History of the Last 2000 Years,* Scribner, New York, 1995.

Lewis, Bernard, *The Crisis of Islam,* the Modern Library, New York, 2003.

Margulis, L. and Sagan, D., *What is Life?,* Simon & Schuster, New York, 1995.

Marx, J., "DNA Replication," *Science,* 270:1585, 1995.

McFadden, John, *Quantum Evolution: Life in the Multiverse,* Flamingo, London, 2000.

# REFERENCES

Mojzsis, S. J., Arrhenius, K. B., et al. "Evidence for life on Earth before 3,800 million years ago," *Nature,* 384, 55-59, 1996.

Moreland, J. P., *The Creation Hypothesis: Scientific Evidence for an Intelligent Designer,* Intervarsity Press, Illinois, 1994.

Newton, I., "General Schohum" in *Mathematical Principles of Natural Philosophy,* Great Books of the Western World, Chicago, 360, 1952.

Norwak, R., "Mining Treasures from Junk DNA," *Science,* 263:608, 1994.

Orgel, L., *The Origins of Life,* Chapman and Hall, London, 1973.

Orgel, L., "The Origin of Life on Earth," *Scientific American,* October, 1994.

Penrose R., *The Emperor's New Mind,* Vintage, London, 1989.

Penrose, R., *Shadows of the Mind,* Vintage, London, 1994.

Crick, Francis, *Life Itself,* Simon & Schuster, New York, 1981.

Report on the Global HIV/AIDS Epidemic, UNAIDS, July 2002.

Ridley, Matt, *Genome, The Autobiography Of A Species in 23 Chapters,* Harper Collins, New York, 1999.

Rose, S., *The Chemistry of Life,* Penguin, London, 1991.

Robinson, Adam, *Bin Laden Behind the Mask of Terrorism,* Mainstream Publishing, Edinburgh, 2001.

Rubin E, Farber, JL., *Pathology,* Philadelphia, J B Lippincott, 1988.

Ruthven, Malise, *ISLAM. A Very Short Introduction,* Oxford University Press, New York, 1997.

Sagan, Carl, *Billions and Billions,* Random House, New York, 1997.

Sagan, Carl and Druyan Ann, *Comet,* Ballantine Books, New York, 1997.

Schrödinger, E., *What is Life?,* Cambridge University Press, Cambridge, 1944.

Schroder, Gerald L., *Genesis and The Big Bang,* Banton Books, New York, 1992.

Schroder, Gerald L., *The Science of God,* Broadway Books, New York, 1997.

Shirer, Williams, *The Rise and Fall of the Third Reich,* Ballantine Books, USA, 1950.

Shipler, David, *Arab and Jew,* Penguin Books, New York, 1987.

Silk, J., *The Big Bang,* W. H. Freeman, New York, 1989.

Swinford, Steven, "I've found God, says man who cracked the genome," *The Sunday Times*, June 11, 2006.

Taylor, E. and Wheeler, J. A., *Spacetime Physics*, W. H. Freeman, San Francisco, 1966.

Tragert, Joseph, *Understanding Iraq*, Alpha, A Pearson Publication Company, Indianapolis, 2003.

UNESCO Draft Report on Embryonic Stem Cells, Paris, 2002.

Varghese, Roy Abraham, *Great Thinkers On Great Questions, One World*, Oxford, 1988.

Varghese, Roy Abraham, *Cosmos, Bios, Theos,* Open Court, Illinois, 1992.

Wald, G., "The Origin Of Life," *Scientific American*, August, 1954.

Waldrop, M., "Did Life Really Start Out in a RNA World?", *Science*, 246:246, December, 1989.

Ward P., and Brownlee D., *Rare Earth*, Copernicus, New York, 2000.

Watson, J., *The Double Helix*, Weidelfeld and Micolson, London, 1968.

Weinberg, S., "Life in the Universe," *Scientific American*, October, 1994.

Wilford, J., "Believers Score in Battle over the Battle of Jericho," *New York Times*, February, 1990.